So you really want ~~to~~

Maths

Book 1

Answer Book

GALORE PARK

www.galorepark.co.uk

Published by Galore Park Publishing Ltd
338 Euston Road, London NW1 3BH
www.galorepark.co.uk

Text copyright © Galore Park
Illustrations copyright © Galore Park 2003
Technical drawings by Graham Edwards

This publication includes images from CorelDRAW ® 9 which are
protected by the copyright laws of the U.S., Canada and elsewhere.
Used under licence.

Typography and layout by Typetechnique, London W1
Cover design by GKA Design, London WC2H
Printed and bound by CPI Group (UK) Ltd, Croydon CR0 4YY

ISBN-13: 978 1 902984 19 3

First published 2004
Reprinted 2004, 2006, 2007, 2008, 2010, 2011, 2012, 2013, 2014

Details of other Galore Park publications are available at
www.galorepark.co.uk

ISEB Revision Guides, publications and examination papers may also be
obtained from Galore Park.

Preface

This set of answers is the result of a huge amount of hard work on the part of Teresa Sibree of Marlborough House School and David Hanson of ISEB. Without them, publication of the book would have been impossible and we are most grateful to them both. Thanks are also due to Michael Ede and Moira Laffey, both of whom gave generously of their time at busy times of the year. Serena and all of us at Galore Park are most grateful.

Please note that in the reprint (2004) of Maths Book 1, changes were made to the following exercises:

Ex. 5.2, Q.5(e); Ex. 6.1, Q.8; Ex. 7.4, Q.2(h); Ex. 7.9, Q.7; Ex. 19.2, Q.5.

The answers in this book reflect those changes.

Contents

Chapter 1: Back to basics 1

Chapter 2: More calculations 7

Chapter 3: Introducing geometry 16

Chapter 4: More about ten 23

Chapter 5: More about numbers 29

Chapter 6: Symmetry 39

Chapter 7: Introducing fractions 45

Chapter 8: Introducing decimals, money and the metric system 51

Chapter 9: Time, travel and tables 57

Chapter 10: Charts and tables 61

Chapter 11: Below zero, or negative numbers 68

Chapter 12: Introducing algebra 75

Chapter 13: Calculating with and without a calculator 79

Chapter 14: More decimals 82

Chapter 15: Area 94

Chapter 16: Triangles, angles and bearings 99

Chapter 17: Percentages 105

Chapter 18: Probability 110

Chapter 19: Shapes in 3 dimensions 114

Chapter 20. Mean, mode and median 119

Chapter 1: Back to basics

Exercise 1.1: Roman numerals

1.
- **(a)** V
- **(b)** X
- **(c)** XI
- **(d)** XXV
- **(e)** CXX
- **(f)** DXL
- **(g)** LVI
- **(h)** CCLV
- **(i)** MCX
- **(j)** DCVII
- **(k)** CDXVII
- **(l)** DCCCLXVII

2.
- **(a)** 3
- **(b)** 9
- **(c)** 8
- **(d)** 20
- **(e)** 9
- **(f)** 24
- **(g)** 250
- **(h)** 620
- **(i)** 155
- **(j)** 45
- **(k)** 2222
- **(l)** 1999

Exercise 1.2 : Revision of basic number bonds

1.

+	2	5	4	3
4	6	9	8	7
1	3	6	5	4
3	5	8	7	6
2	4	7	6	5

+	5	6	8	7
4	9	10	12	11
5	10	11	13	12
3	8	9	11	10
2	7	8	10	9

2. 0 + 10, 1 + 9, 2 + 8, 3 + 7, 4 + 6, 5 + 5, 6 + 4, 7 + 3, 8 + 2, 9 + 1, 10 + 0.

3. 0 + 20, 1 + 19, 2 + 18, 3 + 17, 4 + 16, 5 + 15, 6 + 14, 7 + 13, 8 + 12, 9 + 11, 10 + 10, 11 + 9, 12 + 8, 13 + 7, 14 + 6, 15 + 5, 16 + 4, 17 + 3, 18 + 2, 19 + 1, 20 + 0.

4. **(a)**

+	9	6	7	8
6	15	12	13	14
9	18	15	16	17
8	17	14	15	16
7	16	13	14	15

(b) 18 (9+9)

5.
- **(a)** 7 + 2 = 9
- **(b)** 6 + 3 = 9
- **(c)** 8 + 1 = 9
- **(d)** 5 + 4 = 9
- **(e)** 3 + 5 = 8
- **(f)** 7 + 12 = 19
- **(g)** 6 + 23 = 29
- **(h)** 8 + 11 = 19
- **(i)** 5 + 34 = 39
- **(j)** 3 + 34 = 37

6.
- **(a)** 7 + 5 = 12
- **(b)** 8 + 3 = 11
- **(c)** 6 + 7 = 13
- **(d)** 9 + 4 = 13
- **(e)** 7 + 8 = 15
- **(f)** 7 + 15 = 22
- **(g)** 8 + 23 = 31
- **(h)** 6 + 17 = 23
- **(i)** 9 + 34 = 43
- **(j)** 7 + 28 = 35

7.
- **(a)** 8 + 2 = 10
- **(b)** 6 + 5 = 11
- **(c)** 8 + 7 = 15
- **(d)** 6 + 4 = 10
- **(e)** 7 + 6 = 13
- **(f)** 18 + 22 = 40
- **(g)** 36 + 25 = 61
- **(h)** 28 + 17 = 45
- **(i)** 16 + 34 = 50
- **(j)** 37 + 26 = 63

8.
- **(a)** 26 + 12 = 38
- **(b)** 36 + 63 = 99
- **(c)** 54 + 27 = 81
- **(d)** 16 + 44 = 60
- **(e)** 38 + 26 = 64
- **(f)** 57 + 12 = 69
- **(g)** 66 + 26 = 92
- **(h)** 38 + 18 = 56
- **(i)** 46 + 34 = 80
- **(j)** 45 + 25 = 70

Exercise 1.3

1. (a) 4 + 9 = 13   (e) 3 + 9 = 12
    (b) 8 + 9 = 17   (f) 6 + 9 = 15
    (c) 2 + 9 = 11   (g) 5 + 9 = 14
    (d) 7 + 9 = 16   (h) 9 + 9 = 18

2. (a) 14 + 9 = 23   (e) 73 + 9 = 82
    (b) 28 + 9 = 37   (f) 46 + 9 = 55
    (c) 52 + 9 = 61   (g) 35 + 9 = 44
    (d) 37 + 9 = 46   (h) 39 + 9 = 48

3. (a) 4 + 19 = 23   (e) 3 + 29 = 32
    (b) 8 + 19 = 27   (f) 6 + 39 = 45
    (c) 2 + 19 = 21   (g) 5 + 19 = 24
    (d) 7 + 19 = 26   (h) 9 + 59 = 68

4. (a) 35 + 19 = 54   (e) 29 + 27 = 56
    (b) 29 + 36 = 65   (f) 39 + 78 = 117
    (c) 23 + 49 = 72   (g) 22 + 29 = 51
    (d) 19 + 39 = 58   (h) 54 + 39 = 93

Exercise 1.4

1. (a) 5 + 8 = 13   (d) 9 + 6 = 15   (g) 7 + 4 = 11
         8 + 5 = 13   6 + 9 = 15   4 + 7 = 11
         13 − 5 = 8   15 − 6 = 9   11 − 4 = 7
         13 − 8 = 5   15 − 9 = 6   11 − 7 = 4

    (b) 8 + 7 = 15   (e) 5 + 9 = 14   (h) 6 + 7 = 13
         7 + 8 = 15   9 + 5 = 14   7 + 6 = 13
         15 − 7 = 8   14 − 9 = 5   13 − 7 = 6
         15 − 8 = 7   14 − 5 = 9   13 − 6 = 7

    (c) 3 + 8 = 11   (f) 8 + 6 = 14   (i) 5 + 7 = 12
         8 + 3 = 11   6 + 8 = 14   7 + 5 = 12
         11 − 8 = 3   14 − 6 = 8   12 − 7 = 5
         11 − 3 = 8   14 − 8 = 6   12 − 5 = 7

2. (a)

−	12	15	14	13
5	7	10	9	8
8	4	7	6	5
7	5	8	7	6
3	9	12	11	10

(b)

−	15	17	16	19
6	9	11	10	13
9	6	8	7	10
8	7	9	8	11
5	10	12	11	14

3. (a) 7 − 2 = 5   (g) 6 − 3 = 3   (m) 8 − 2 = 6
    (b) 17 − 2 = 15   (h) 16 − 3 = 13   (n) 18 − 2 = 16
    (c) 17 − 12 = 5   (i) 16 − 13 = 3   (o) 58 − 32 = 26
    (d) 8 − 3 = 5   (j) 9 − 5 = 4   (p) 7 − 4 = 3
    (e) 18 − 3 = 15   (k) 19 − 5 = 14   (q) 17 − 4 = 13
    (f) 48 − 13 = 35   (l) 49 − 25 = 24   (r) 67 − 34 = 33

4. (a)

−	85	57	63	72
18	67	39	45	54
36	49	21	27	36
29	56	28	34	43
47	38	10	16	25

(b)

−	86	63	71	95
55	31	8	16	40
38	48	25	33	57
46	40	17	25	49
25	61	38	46	70

Exercise 1.5

1. **(a)**

+	15	36	44	28	36
27	42	63	71	55	63
35	50	71	79	63	71
46	61	82	90	74	82
19	34	55	63	47	55
24	39	60	68	52	60

(b)

−	37	46	51	59	31
16	21	30	35	43	15
27	10	19	24	32	4
31	6	15	20	28	0
29	8	17	22	30	2
18	19	28	33	41	13

2.

+	26	48	17	56	36	61	77	37
42	68	90	59	98	78	103	119	79
57	83	105	74	113	93	118	134	94
18	44	66	35	74	54	79	95	55
68	94	116	85	124	104	129	145	105
49	75	97	66	105	85	110	126	86
24	50	72	41	80	60	85	101	61
38	64	86	55	94	74	99	115	75
75	101	123	92	131	111	136	152	112

3.

−	26	48	17	56	36	61	77	37
42	16	6	25	14	6	19	35	5
57	31	9	40	1	21	4	20	20
18	8	30	1	38	18	43	59	19
68	42	20	51	12	32	7	9	31
49	23	1	32	7	13	12	28	12
24	2	24	7	32	12	37	53	13
38	12	10	21	18	2	23	39	1
75	49	27	58	19	39	14	2	38

4. **(a)**

+	11	24	26	37	18
38	49	62	64	75	56
37	48	61	63	74	55
29	40	53	55	66	47
45	56	69	71	82	63
32	43	56	58	69	50

(b)

−	43	36	35	4	64
27	16	9	8	23	37
61	18	25	26	57	3
51	8	15	16	47	13
19	24	17	16	15	45
47	4	11	12	43	17

Exercise 1.6

1. (a) 1 + 99 = 100   (d) 4 + 96 = 100   (g) 7 + 93 = 100
    (b) 2 + 98 = 100   (e) 5 + 95 = 100   (h) 8 + 92 = 100
    (c) 3 + 97 = 100   (f) 6 + 94 = 100   (i) 9 + 91 = 100

2. (a) 16 + 84 = 100   (d) 13 + 87 = 100   (g) 17 + 83 = 100
    (b) 11 + 89 = 100   (e) 15 + 85 = 100   (h) 19 + 81 = 100
    (c) 18 + 82 = 100   (f) 12 + 88 = 100   (i) 14 + 86 = 100

3. (a) 15 + 85 = 100   (d) 32 + 68 = 100   (g) 49 + 51 = 100
    (b) 59 + 41 = 100   (e) 26 + 74 = 100   (h) 43 + 57 = 100
    (c) 21 + 79 = 100   (f) 54 + 46 = 100   (i) 37 + 63 = 100

4. (a) 41 + 159 = 200   (d) 466 + 134 = 600   (g) 94 + 106 = 200
    (b) 108 + 192 = 300   (e 132 + 668 = 800   (h) 27 + 373 = 400
    (c) 305 + 195 = 500   (f) 199 + 101 = 300   (i) 323 + 277 = 600

5. (a) 195 + 23 = 218   (g) 186 + 59 = 245   (m) 174 + 62 = 236
    (b) 163 + 49 = 212   (h) 151 + 67 = 218   (n) 148 + 71 = 219
    (c) 135 + 82 = 217   (i) 178 + 53 = 231   (o) 156 + 99 = 255
    (d) 154 + 73 = 227   (j) 192 + 82 = 274   (p) 168 + 75 = 243
    (e) 236 + 64 = 300   (k) 315 + 38 = 353   (q) 425 + 58 = 483
    (f) 672 + 39 = 711   (l) 476 + 27 = 503   (r) 619 + 84 = 703

Exercise 1.7

1.

+	−
plus	down
more	minus
increased	subtract
rose	lower
add	away
total	decreased
joined	dropped
greater	difference
up	less
addition	
another	

2.

+	−
gained	fell
grew	diminished
received	took away
joined	fewer
captured	subtraction
	lost
	escaped
	gave away
	separated

3. 75 stickers
4. 140 km
5. 58 children
6. 28 cm
7. £23
8. 16 people
9. 45 cm
10. plus, minus
    more, less
    increased, decreased
    rose, fell
    add, subtract
    greater, fewer
    up, down.
    add, subtract
    gained, lost
    joined, separated

Exercise 1.8

1. 16
2. 12
3. 62
4. 82
5. £41
6. 44 km
7. 56 children
8. 79 pages
9. 55 or 89. Which house had most points.
10. 23 points

Exercise 1.9:
Extension questions

1. 40p
2. 13 boys
3. 11 years old
4. 86p
5. £13
6. 43 marks
7. 12 house points
8. 56p
9. 28p
10. 18p
11. 15p

Summary exercise: Exercise 1.10

1. (a) XXV   (b) CCXXV   (c) MMCCXXV
2. (a) 1520   (b) 1200   (c) 35

3.
(a) $19 + 7 = 26$
(b) $15 + 29 = 44$
(c) $25 + 46 = 71$
(d) $58 + 26 = 84$

4.
(a) $19 - 8 = 11$
(b) $17 - 9 = 8$
(c) $35 - 27 = 8$
(d) $56 - 39 = 17$

5. (a)

+	9	27	8	19
26	35	53	34	45
13	22	40	21	32
35	44	62	43	54
17	26	44	25	36

(b)

−	23	17	11	45
9	14	8	2	36
15	8	2	4	30
25	2	8	14	20
46	23	29	35	1

6. 62 children
7. 43 house points
8. 12 years old
9. 24p

End of chapter activities: Roman numeral investigations

Longest years

1. MDCCCLXXXVIII (1888)
2. One thousand
3. XXVIII (28)
4. MCMXCV (1995)

How many numbers?

5. All numbers from 1 to 39. 2 (XIV, XVI)
6. All numbers from 1 to 89.   4 (XLIV, XLVI, LXIV, LXVI)
7. 4 (CXLIV, CXLVI, CLXIV, CLXVI). Difference is 22.
8. 8 (CDXLIV, CDXLVI, CDLXIV, CDLXVI, DCXLIV, DCXLVI, DCLXIV, DCLXVI).
   Difference is 222.
9. 8 (MCDXLIV, MCDXLVI, MCDLXIV, MCDLXVI, MDCXLIV, MDCXLVI, MDCLXIV, MDCLXVI).
   Difference is 222.

10.

No. of numerals	No. of numbers	Highest	Lowest	Difference
2	2	VI	IV	2 or II
3	2	XVI	XIV	2 or II
4	4	LXVI	XLIV	22 or XXII
5	4	CLXVI	CXLIV	22 or XXII
6	8	DCLXVI	CDXLIV	222 or CCXXII
7	8	MDCLXVI	MCDXLIV	222 or CCXXII
8	16	ZMDCLXVI	MZCDXLIV	2222 or MMCCXXII

Where Z = 5000

Chapter 2: More calculations

Exercise 2.1

1.

×	2	3	4	5	6	7	8	9	10	11	12
2	4	6	8	10	12	14	16	18	20	22	24
3	6	9	12	15	18	21	24	27	30	33	36
4	8	12	16	20	24	28	32	36	40	44	48
5	10	15	20	25	30	35	40	45	50	55	60
6	12	18	24	30	36	42	48	54	60	66	72
7	14	21	28	35	42	49	56	63	70	77	84
8	16	24	32	40	48	56	64	72	80	88	96
9	18	27	36	45	54	63	72	81	90	99	108
10	20	30	40	50	60	70	80	90	100	110	120
11	22	33	44	55	66	77	88	99	110	121	132
12	24	36	48	60	72	84	96	108	120	132	144

2.

×	6	4	7	5	11	8	2	12	10	3	9
4	24	16	28	20	44	32	8	48	40	12	36
10	60	40	70	50	110	80	20	120	100	30	90
8	48	32	56	40	88	64	16	96	80	24	72
12	72	48	84	60	132	96	24	144	120	36	108
2	12	8	14	10	22	16	4	24	20	6	18
7	42	28	49	35	77	56	14	84	70	21	63
5	30	20	35	25	55	40	10	60	50	15	45
11	66	44	77	55	121	88	22	132	110	33	99
9	54	36	63	45	99	72	18	108	90	27	81
3	18	12	21	15	33	24	6	36	30	9	27
6	36	24	42	30	66	48	12	72	60	18	54

3.
(a) $72 \div 8 = 9$
(b) $18 \div 2 = 9$
(c) $49 \div 7 = 7$
(d) $32 \div 8 = 4$
(e) $63 \div 9 = 7$

(f) $24 \div 3 = 8$
(g) $36 \div 4 = 9$
(h) $60 \div 5 = 12$
(i) $42 \div 6 = 7$
(j) $48 \div 8 = 6$

4.
(a) $78 \div 8 = 9 \text{ r } 6$
(b) $19 \div 2 = 9 \text{ r } 1$
(c) $52 \div 7 = 7 \text{ r } 3$
(d) $36 \div 8 = 4 \text{ r } 4$
(e) $68 \div 9 = 7 \text{ r } 5$

(f) $26 \div 3 = 8 \text{ r } 2$
(g) $37 \div 4 = 9 \text{ r } 1$
(h) $63 \div 5 = 12 \text{ r } 3$
(i) $47 \div 6 = 7 \text{ r } 5$
(j) $52 \div 8 = 6 \text{ r } 4$

5.
(a) $78 \div 9 = 8 \text{ r } 6$
(b) $23 \div 3 = 7 \text{ r } 2$
(c) $62 \div 8 = 7 \text{ r } 6$
(d) $45 \div 6 = 7 \text{ r } 3$
(e) $27 \div 4 = 6 \text{ r } 3$

(f) $28 \div 3 = 9 \text{ r } 1$
(g) $42 \div 5 = 8 \text{ r } 2$
(h) $31 \div 4 = 7 \text{ r } 3$
(i) $62 \div 9 = 6 \text{ r } 8$
(j) $61 \div 7 = 8 \text{ r } 5$

6.
(a) $63 \div 5 = 12 \text{ r } 3$
(b) $48 \div 5 = 9 \text{ r } 3$
(c) $24 \div 3 = 8 \text{ r } 0$
(d) $48 \div 8 = 6 \text{ r } 0$
(e) $56 \div 7 = 8 \text{ r } 0$

(f) $27 \div 4 = 6 \text{ r } 3$
(g) $56 \div 9 = 6 \text{ r } 2$
(h) $49 \div 5 = 9 \text{ r } 4$
(i) $35 \div 7 = 5 \text{ r } 0$
(j) $54 \div 8 = 6 \text{ r } 6$

7.

÷	24	48	12	30	36
2	12	24	6	15	18
8	3	6	✗	✗	✗
4	6	12	3	✗	9
6	4	8	2	5	6
12	2	4	1	✗	3

Exercise 2.2

1.
(a) $2 \times 5 = 10$
(b) $2 \times 8 = 16$
(c) $2 \times 4 = 8$

(d) $2 \times 7 = 14$
(e) $2 \times 6 = 12$
(f) $2 \times 9 = 18$

2.
(a) $2 \times 15 = 30$
(b) $2 \times 18 = 36$
(c) $2 \times 14 = 28$

(d) $2 \times 17 = 34$
(e) $2 \times 16 = 32$
(f) $2 \times 19 = 38$

3.
(a) $2 \times 21 = 42$
(b) $2 \times 33 = 66$
(c) $2 \times 45 = 90$
(d) $2 \times 25 = 50$
(e) $2 \times 38 = 76$
(f) $2 \times 44 = 88$

(g) $2 \times 34 = 68$
(h) $2 \times 41 = 82$
(i) $2 \times 22 = 44$
(j) $2 \times 37 = 74$
(k) $2 \times 46 = 92$
(l) $2 \times 29 = 58$

4.
(a) $26 + 27 = 53$
(b) $38 + 37 = 75$
(c) $19 + 18 = 37$
(d) $35 + 37 = 72$
(e) $71 + 74 = 145$

(f) $52 + 53 = 105$
(g) $46 + 45 = 91$
(h) $99 + 97 = 196$
(i) $64 + 66 = 130$
(j) $87 + 85 = 172$

Exercise 2.3

1. (a) Two thousand, three hundred and five.

    (b) Thirteen thousand, four hundred and fifty.

    (c) One hundred thousand, two hundred and fifty.

    (d) Three hundred and three thousand, four hundred and nineteen.

    (e) Thirty thousand, four hundred and one.

    (f) Thirty-four thousand, five hundred and seventeen.

    (g) Three million, four hundred and fifty-one thousand, two hundred and thirty-seven.

    (h) Nine hundred and ninety-nine thousand and nine.

    (i) Nineteen million, four hundred and two thousand, four hundred and thirty.

    (j) Five hundred and five million and four.

2. (a) 419   (f) 18 000 060

    (b) 16 529   (g) 25 050 018

    (c) 70 008   (h) 108 307 102

    (d) 260 704   (i) 600 000 409

    (e) 3 479 368   (j) 9 005 006

Exercise 2.4

1. (a) 30   (f) 400

    (b) 300   (g) 5000

    (c) 800   (h) 60

    (d) 3000   (i) 700

    (e) 40   (j) 3000

2. (a) $40 + 570 \rightarrow 610 \rightarrow 600$ (f) $300 - 30 \rightarrow 270 \rightarrow 300$

    (b) $4000 + 70 \rightarrow 4070 \rightarrow 4100$ (g) $6500 - 3200 \rightarrow 3300$

    (c) $300 + 700 \rightarrow 1000$ (h) $5600 + 300 + 500 \rightarrow 6400$

    (d) $3400 + 500 + 0 \rightarrow 3900$ (i) $4500 - 1000 \rightarrow 3500$

    (e) $500 + 3500 + 100 \rightarrow 4100$ (j) $1000 + 100 + 10\ 000 \rightarrow 11\ 100$

Exercise 2.5

1.   37 + 451 = 488
2.   146 + 520 = 666
3.   345 + 789 = 1134
4.   309 + 19 = 328
5.   4534 + 328 = 4862
6.   345 + 326 = 671
7.   19 + 4532 = 4551
8.   346 + 3291 = 3637
9.   345 + 287 + 19 = 651
10.   543 + 606 + 9 = 1158
11.   27 + 451 + 89 = 567
12.   2477 + 910 + 46 = 3433
13.   3503 + 1570 + 305 = 5378
14.   1965 + 1852 + 67 = 3884
15.   23 + 564 + 789 + 5642 = 7018
16.   7899 + 8 + 93 + 387 + 645 = 9032

Exercise 2.6

1.   48 − 17 = 31
2.   63 − 19 = 44
3.   352 − 125 = 227
4.   474 − 165 = 309
5.   358 − 137 = 221
6.   635 − 367 = 268
7.   815 − 386 = 429
8.   629 − 454 = 175
9.   735 − 52 = 683
10.   3489 − 734 = 2755

Exercise 2.7

1.   405 − 167 = 238
2.   302 − 188 = 114
3.   790 − 345 = 445
4.   607 − 420 = 187
5.   504 − 458 = 46
6.   4506 − 1788 = 2718
7.   8064 − 3786 = 4278
8.   7001 − 4578 = 2423
9.   8005 − 3738 = 4267
10.   6004 − 5764 = 240

Exercise 2.8

1.   32 × 3 = 96
2.   24 × 2 = 48
3.   47 × 3 = 141
4.   26 × 5 = 130
5.   122 × 4 = 488
6.   31 × 6 = 186
7.   32 × 7 = 224
8.   53 × 8 = 424
9.   22 × 9 = 198
10.   216 × 6 = 1296
11.   243 × 5 = 1215
12.   346 × 2 = 692
13.   368 × 4 = 1472
14.   432 × 5 = 2160
15.   836 × 4 = 3344
16.   318 × 8 = 2544
17.   425 × 7 = 2975
18.   627 × 8 = 5016
19.   525 × 9 = 4725
20.   845 × 7 = 5915

Exercise 2.9

1.	$69 \div 3 = 23$		6.	$245 \div 5 = 49$
2.	$64 \div 2 = 32$		7.	$418 \div 2 = 209$
3.	$84 \div 3 = 28$		8.	$836 \div 4 = 209$
4.	$85 \div 5 = 17$		9.	$535 \div 5 = 107$
5.	$324 \div 4 = 81$		10.	$927 \div 3 = 309$
11.	$96 \div 6 = 16$		16.	$896 \div 8 = 112$
12.	$91 \div 7 = 13$		17.	$406 \div 7 = 58$
13.	$168 \div 8 = 21$		18.	$824 \div 8 = 103$
14.	$549 \div 9 = 61$		19.	$963 \div 9 = 107$
15.	$456 \div 6 = 76$		20.	$735 \div 7 = 105$
21.	$84 \div 6 = 14$		26.	$692 \div 8 = 86$ r 4
22.	$87 \div 7 = 12$ r 3		27.	$836 \div 7 = 119$ r 3
23.	$258 \div 8 = 32$ r 2		28.	$945 \div 8 = 118$ r 1
24.	$617 \div 9 = 68$ r 5		29.	$297 \div 9 = 33$
25.	$815 \div 6 = 135$ r 5		30.	$816 \div 7 = 116$ r 4

Exercise 2.10

1.	24 children		9.	90 loaves of bread
2.	6 teachers		10.	144 eggs
3.	7 teachers		11.	39 full weeks
4.	54 children		12.	43 groups
5.	1115 tokens		13.	29 parents
6.	504 children		14.	3538 books
7.	687 points		15.	18 rulers
8.	115 points		16.	24 glue sticks

Exercise 2.11: Extension questions

1. | 7 | × | **4** | = | 2 | 8 |

2. | 3 | 6 | ÷ | **9** | = | 4 |

3. | 6 | 5 | ÷ | **9** | = | 7 | r2 |

4. | 5 | 8 | ÷ | **6** | = | 9 | r4 |

5. | 4 | 8 | ÷ | **9** | = | **5** | r3 | or | 4 | 8 | ÷ | **5** | = | **9** | r3 |

6. | **3** | 4 | ÷ | 8 | = | **4** | r2 |

7. | **3** | 3 | ÷ | 7 | = | **4** | r5 |

8. | 2 | **3** | × | 2 | = | **4** | 6 | or

   | 2 | **8** | × | 2 | = | **5** | 6 |

9. | 7 | **2** | ÷ | 2 | = | **3** | 6 |

10. | **1** | 8 | × | 2 | = | 3 | 6 |

11.
	H	T	U	
	2	**5**	3	
+	**3**	3	**4**	
	5	8	7	

12.
	H	T	U	
	4	**0**	6	
+	**2**	7	7	
	6	8	3	

Exercise 2.12

1.

	H	T	U	
	4	**7**	8	
+	1	7	**7**	
	6	5	5	

2.

	H	T	U	
	6	**8**	5	
−	**2**	3	**7**	
	4	4	8	

3.

	H	T	U	
	1	**8**	1	
		×	**3**	
	5	4	3	

4.

	H	T	U	
	2	4	**2**	
4	**9**	6	8	

5.

	H	T	U	
	4	**6**	7	
−	**1**	4	**2**	
	3	2	5	

6.

	H	T	U	
	5	**1**	3	
−	3	4	**8**	
	1	6	5	

7.

	H	T	U	
	1	**4**	4	
		×	**2**	
	2	8	**8**	

8.

	H	T	U	
	1	**2**	8	
6	**7**	6	**8**	

Exercise 2.13: Summary exercise

1.

×	5	8	7	6
9	45	72	63	54
11	55	88	77	66
7	35	56	49	42
4	20	32	28	24

2. **(a)** $35 \div 5 = 7$ **(f)** $42 \div 6 = 7$

     (b) $48 \div 8 = 6$ **(g)** $24 \div 3 = 8$

     (c) $35 \div 6 = 5 \text{ r } 5$ **(h)** $58 \div 9 = 6 \text{ r } 4$

     (d) $63 \div 8 = 7 \text{ r } 7$ **(i)** $62 \div 7 = 8 \text{ r } 6$

     (e) $35 \div 4 = 8 \text{ r } 3$ **(j)** $80 \div 9 = 8 \text{ r } 8$

3. **(a)** $245 + 457 = 702$ **(b)** $3478 + 672 + 19 = 4169$

4. **(a)** $367 - 148 = 219$ **(b)** $5005 - 1437 = 3568$

5. **(a)** $146 \times 4 = 584$ **(b)** $468 \times 7 = 3276$

6. **(a)** $476 \div 4 = 119$ **(b)** $619 \div 3 = 206 \text{ r } 1$ **(c)** $985 \div 7 = 140 \text{ r } 5$

7. 6 sweets

8. 72 maths books

9. 190

10. 216 apples

11. 12 chocolates

12. **(a)**

9	×	8	=	7	2

     (b)

4	7	÷	9	=	5	r2

     (c)

3	9	+	5	5	=	9	4

     (d)

	H	T	U
	1	4	5
+	5	6	8
	7	1	3

     (e)

	H	T	U
	1	3	4
		×	6
	8	0	4

or

	H	T	U
	1	3	9
		×	6
	8	3	4

End of chapter activity: What's in the box?

1. **(a)**
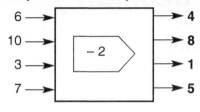

6 → → 4
10 → → 8
3 → − 2 → 1
7 → → 5

(b)

8 → → 2
16 → → 4
4 → ÷ 4 → 1
12 → → 3

2. **(a)**
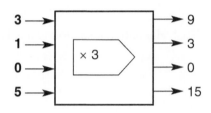

3 → → 9
1 → → 3
0 → × 3 → 0
5 → → 15

(b)

3 → → 6
4 → → 7
9 → + 3 → 12
5 → → 8

3. **(a)** × 4 **(b)** − 3
(c) × 2 **(d)** ÷ 3

4. **(a)**
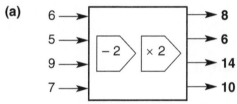

6 → → 8
5 → → 6
9 → − 2 → × 2 → 14
7 → → 10

(b)

6 → → 6
8 → → 7
2 → ÷ 2 → + 3 → 4
16 → → 11

5. **(a)**
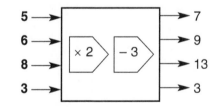

5 → → 7
6 → → 9
8 → × 2 → − 3 → 13
3 → → 3

(b)

5 → → 12
4 → → 9
7 → − 1 → × 3 → 18
2 → → 3

6. **(a)** − 2, × 2 or × 2, − 4 **(c)** × 3, − 2
(b) ÷ 2, +1 or +2, ÷ 2 **(d)** − 1, × 4 or × 4, − 4

Chapter 3: Introducing geometry

Exercise 3.1: The calendar of the ancients

1. Winter solstice: Christmas Day.

   Summer solstice: Midsummer's Day, Father's Day.

   Spring equinox: Easter is the first Sunday after the full moon on or after 21st March (named after the festival of the goddess Eostre). Mothering Sunday.

   Autumn equinox: Harvest Festival (September 21st), Rosh Hashanah falls around this time, as does the Chinese Moon Festival.

2. Early February, May, August and November.

3. February 2nd: Candlemas Day, Groundhog Day

   May 1st: May Day

   August 1-2nd: No longer celebrated but was Lammas Day, the start of the harvest.

   November 5th: Guy Fawkes; End October; All Saints' and All Souls (Halloween); Diwali falls around here.

Exercise 3.2: The geometry of the ancients

Practical

Exercise 3.3

1. Acute angle 45°

2. Obtuse angle 122°

3. Acute angle 71°

4. Acute angle 53°

5. Reflex angle 325°

6. Obtuse angle 136°

7. Acute angle 84°

8. Reflex angle 253°

Exercise 3.4

1. Measure the sides of the triangles and write the measurement neatly on each side.
2. Measure the angles of each triangle and write the angle neatly in each angle.
3. Under each triangle write if it is scalene, right-angled, isosceles, obtuse-angled or equilateral.

1.

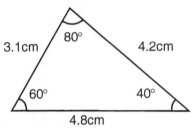

3.1cm 80° 4.2cm 60° 40° 4.8cm

Scalene triangle

2.

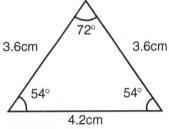

72° 3.6cm 3.6cm 54° 54° 4.2cm

Isosceles triangle

3.

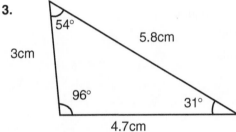

54° 5.8cm 3cm 96° 31° 4.7cm

Obtuse-angled triangle

4.

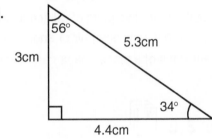

56° 5.3cm 3cm 34° 4.4cm

Right-angled triangle

5.

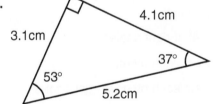

4.1cm 3.1cm 37° 53° 5.2cm

Right-angled triangle

6.

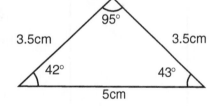

95° 3.5cm 3.5cm 42° 43° 5cm

Obtuse-angled triangle

7.

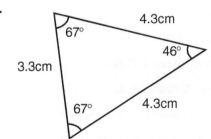

4.3cm 67° 46° 3.3cm 67° 4.3cm

Isosceles triangle

8.

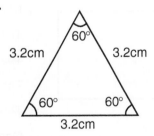

60° 3.2cm 3.2cm 60° 60° 3.2cm

Equilateral triangle

Exercise 3.5

1. Rectangle and parallelogram

2. Kite

3. Rhombus

4. Isosceles trapezium

5. Rectangle

6. Trapezium

7. Trapezium

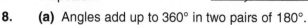
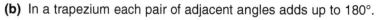

8. **(a)** Angles add up to 360° in two pairs of 180°.

   (b) In a trapezium each pair of adjacent angles adds up to 180°.

9. In a kite there are two pairs of adjacent sides which are equal.
   In a kite there is only one pair of angles which is equal.

10. Adjacent sides of a plane shape can never be parallel.

Exercise 3.6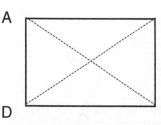

1.

A ⬚ B   Name: Square

The diagonals are equal.

The diagonals meet at right angles.

The diagonals bisect each other.

The diagonals bisect each other at right angles.

D ⬚ C   ~~One diagonal only is bisected by the other~~.

2.

A ⬚ B Name: Rectangle

The diagonals are equal.

~~The diagonals meet at right angles.~~

The diagonals bisect each other.

D ⬚ C ~~The diagonals bisect each other at right angles.~~

~~One diagonal only is bisected by the other.~~

3.

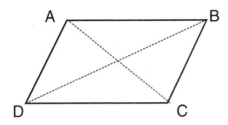

Name: Parallelogram

~~The diagonals are equal.~~

~~The diagonals meet at right angles.~~

The diagonals bisect each other.

~~The diagonals bisect each other at right angles.~~

~~One diagonal only is bisected by the other.~~

4.

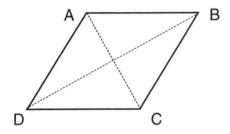

Name: Rhombus

~~The diagonals are equal.~~

The diagonals meet at right angles.

The diagonals bisect each other.

The diagonals bisect each other at right angles.

~~One diagonal only is bisected by the other.~~

5.

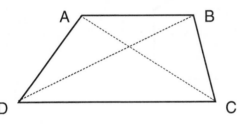

Name: Trapezium

~~The diagonals are equal.~~

~~The diagonals meet at right angles.~~

~~The diagonals bisect each other.~~

~~The diagonals bisect each other at right angles.~~

~~One diagonal only is bisected by the other.~~

6.

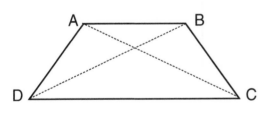

Name: Isosceles trapezium

The diagonals are equal.

~~The diagonals meet at right angles.~~

~~The diagonals bisect each other.~~

~~The diagonals bisect each other at right angles.~~

~~One diagonal only is bisected by the other.~~

7.

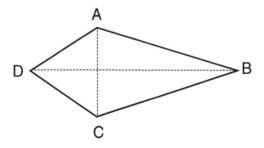

Name: Kite

~~The diagonals are equal.~~

The diagonals meet at right angles.

~~The diagonals bisect each other.~~

The diagonals intersect at right angles.

One diagonal only is bisected by the other.

Exercise 3.7

1. Square
2. Rectangle
3. Trapezium, Kite

4. Check pupils' drawings e.g

5. Check pupils' drawings e.g.

6. 120°

7.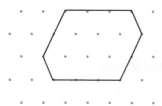

8. (a)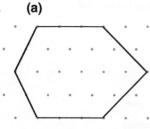

(b)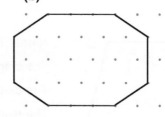

(c)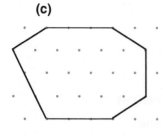

(d)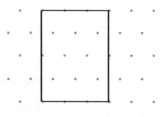

(e)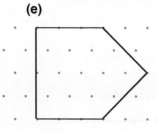

(f) Check pupils' drawings have 6 sides

(g) Check pupils' drawings have 8 sides.

Exercise 3.8: Summary exercise

1. **(a)** Obtuse

   (b) Acute

   (c) Reflex

2. Misread the protractor. 117°

3. 182°, 183° or 184°

4. Isosceles triangle

5. **(a)** Parallelogram

   (b) Rhombus

6. Rhombus

7. Rhombus

8. **(a)** Check pupils' drawings. Various answers possible.

   (b) Check pupils' drawings.

9.

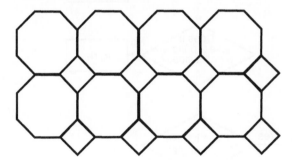

End of chapter 3 activity: Sorting shapes

1. Check pupils' answers.
2.

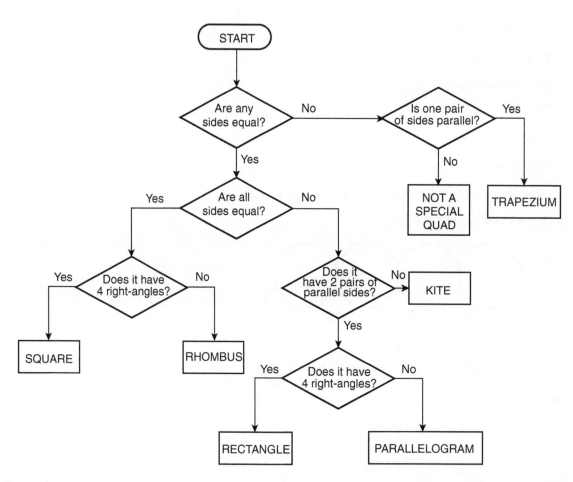

Note: other answers are possible.

Chapter 4: More about ten

Exercise 4.1

1. $40 \times 10 = 400$
2. $60 \times 100 = 6000$
3. $200 \times 1000 = 200\ 000$
4. $600 \times 100 = 60\ 000$
5. $702 \times 100 = 70\ 200$
6. $3004 \times 1000 = 3\ 004\ 000$
7. $820 \times 100 = 82\ 000$
8. $450 \times 1000 = 450\ 000$
9. $602 \times 10 = 6\ 020$
10. $8050 \times 100 = 805\ 000$

Exercise 4.2

1. $400 \div 10 = 40$
2. $400 \div 100 = 4$
3. $200 \div 10 = 20$
4. $60 \div 10 = 6$
5. $7000 \div 100 = 70$
6. $30\ 000 \div 100 = 300$
7. $800 \div 100 = 8$
8. $400\ 000 \div 100 = 4\ 000$
9. $6\ 000\ 000 \div 1000 = 6\ 000$
10. $80\ 000 \div 1000 = 80$

Exercise 4.3

1. $40 \times 30 = 1\ 200$
2. $60 \times 700 = 42\ 000$
3. $200 \times 90 = 18\ 000$
4. $600 \times 4 = 2\ 400$
5. $70 \times 400 = 28\ 000$
6. $30 \times 8000 = 240\ 000$
7. $800 \times 20 = 16\ 000$
8. $400 \times 200 = 80\ 000$
9. $600 \times 20 = 12\ 000$
10. $8000 \times 400 = 3\ 200\ 000$

Exercise 4.4

1. $120 \div 30 = 4$
2. $4200 \div 700 = 6$
3. $18\ 000 \div 90 = 200$
4. $1600 \div 4 = 400$
5. $7200 \div 800 = 9$
6. $32\ 000 \div 80 = 400$
7. $18\ 000 \div 200 = 90$
8. $12\ 000 \div 200 = 60$
9. $1600 \div 20 = 80$
10. $4000 \div 500 = 8$

Exercise 4.5

1. $40 \times 50 = 2\ 000$
2. $200 \times 50 = 10\ 000$
3. $500 \times 60 = 30\ 000$
4. $20 \times 5000 = 100\ 000$
5. $300 \times 400 = 120\ 000$
6. $8000 \times 500 = 4\ 000\ 000$
7. $40 \times 30 \times 400 = 480\ 000$
8. $400 \times 500 \times 300 = 60\ 000\ 000$
9. $5000 \times 40 \times 900 = 180\ 000\ 000$
10. $300 \times 400 \times 50 = 6\ 000\ 000$
11. $30 \times 4000 \times 5 = 600\ 000$
12. $600 \times 400 \times 500 = 120\ 000\ 000$

Exercise 4.6

1.	$400 \div 2 = 200$	7.	$48\ 000 \div 6000 = 8$
2.	$8000 \div 4 = 2\ 000$	8.	$640\ 000 \div 80 = 8\ 000$
3.	$600 \div 20 = 30$	9.	$1\ 000\ 000 \div 50 = 200\ 000$
4.	$4000 \div 5 = 800$	10.	$2\ 000\ 000 \div 400 = 5\ 000$
5.	$6000 \div 50 = 120$	11.	$45\ 000 \div 90 = 500$
6.	$36\ 000 \div 600 = 60$	12.	$3000 \div 60 = 50$

Exercise 4.7

1. $32 \times 59 \approx 30 \times 60 = 1\ 800$ fair

2. $29 \times 99 \approx 30 \times 100 = 3\ 000$ too high

3. $102 \times 52 \approx 100 \times 50 = 5\ 000$ too low

4. $7 \times 503 \approx 7 \times 500 = 3\ 500$ fair

5. $52 \times 38 \approx 50 \times 40 = 2\ 000$ fair

6. $310 \times 49 \approx 300\ \ 50 = 15\ 000$ fair

7. $612 \times 72 \approx 600 \times 70 = 42\ 000$ too low

8. $590 \times 620 \approx 600 \times 600 = 360\ 000$ fair

9. $4012 \times 62 \approx 4\ 000 \times 60 = 240\ 000$ too low

10. $4\ 200 \times 3\ 800 \approx 4\ 000 \times 4\ 000 = 16\ 000\ 000$ fair

Exercise 4.8

1. **(a)** $42 \div 38 = 1.105$

Estimate: **(i)** $40 \div 38 = 1.053$ **(ii)** $40 \div 40 = 1$ **(iii)** $40 \div 36 = 1.111$

(b) $42 \div 32 = 1.3125$

Estimate: **(i)** $40 \div 28 = 1.429$ **(ii)** $40 \div 30 = 1.3$ **(iii)** $40 \div 32 = 1.25$

2. **(a)** Answer (iii) gave the best estimate because both numbers were reduced.

(b) Answer (ii) gave the best estimate because both numbers were reduced.

Exercise 4.9

1. $20 = 2 \times 10^1$
2. $300 = 3 \times 10^2$
3. $4000 = 4 \times 10^3$
4. $5000 = 5 \times 10^3$
5. $30\ 000 = 3 \times 10^4$
6. $40 = 4 \times 10^1$
7. $3000 = 3 \times 10^3$
8. $400\ 000 = 4 \times 10^5$
9. $60\ 000 = 6 \times 10^4$
10. $700 = 7 \times 10^2$
11. $3\ 000\ 000 = 3 \times 10^6$
12. $400\ 000\ 000 = 4 \times 10^8$
13. $30\ 000\ 000\ 000 = 3 \times 10^{10}$
14. $6000 = 6 \times 10^3$
15. $10 = 1 \times 10^1$
16. $500\ 000 = 5 \times 10^5$
17. $900 = 9 \times 10^2$
18. $80\ 000 = 8 \times 10^4$

Exercise 4.10

1. $27 \times 20 = 540$
2. $32 \times 30 = 960$
3. $61 \times 40 = 2440$
4. $45 \times 30 = 1350$
5. $72 \times 60 = 4320$
6. $24 \times 70 = 1680$
7. $37 \times 80 = 2960$
8. $42 \times 90 = 3780$
9. $67 \times 70 = 4690$
10. $54 \times 60 = 3240$

Exercise 4.11

1. $24 \times 50 = 1200$
2. $35 \times 20 = 700$
3. $61 \times 50 = 3050$
4. $45 \times 80 = 3600$
5. $72 \times 50 = 3600$
6. $25 \times 50 = 1250$
7. $35 \times 60 = 2100$
8. $42 \times 50 = 2100$
9. $65 \times 40 = 2600$
10. $54 \times 50 = 2700$
11. $45 \times 300 = 13\ 500$
12. $67 \times 400 = 26\ 800$
13. $39 \times 500 = 19\ 500$
14. $52 \times 500 = 26\ 000$
15. $64 \times 800 = 51\ 200$
16. $127 \times 600 = 76\ 200$
17. $346 \times 500 = 173\ 000$
18. $542 \times 700 = 379\ 400$
19. $408 \times 800 = 326\ 400$
20. $506 \times 500 = 253\ 000$

Exercise 4.12

1. $36 \times 27 = 972$
2. $68 \times 54 = 3\ 672$
3. $73 \times 78 = 5\ 694$
4. $123 \times 83 = 10\ 209$
5. $302 \times 46 = 13\ 892$
6. $307 \times 62 = 19\ 034$
7. $415 \times 35 = 14\ 525$
8. $304 \times 72 = 21\ 888$
9. $806 \times 68 = 54\ 808$
10. $612 \times 35 = 21\ 420$
11. $256 \times 91 = 23\ 296$
12. $440 \times 37 = 16\ 280$

Exercise 4.13

1. 8 760 hours in a year.
2. 86 400 seconds in a day.
3. 744 hours in January.
4. 812 children
5. £3 380
6. 518 miles

Exercise 4.14

1. 13 824 passengers
2. 1840 pizzas
3. 63 hours
4. 361 people
5. 912 children
6. £11.59

Exercise 4.15

1. $832 \div 26 = 32$
2. $703 \div 19 = 37$
3. $936 \div 39 = 24$
4. $966 \div 23 = 42$
5. $408 \div 17 = 24$
6. $938 \div 27 = 34$ r20
7. $839 \div 71 = 11$ r58
8. $917 \div 38 = 24$ r5
9. $568 \div 41 = 13$ r35
10. $840 \div 65 = 12$ r60

Exercise 4.16

11. $2538 \div 54 = 47$
12. $2523 \div 87 = 29$
13. $5704 \div 46 = 124$
14. $9135 \div 63 = 145$
15. $9633 \div 39 = 247$
16. $8208 \div 27 = 304$
17. $4507 \div 71 = 63$ r34
18. $3906 \div 38 = 102$ r30
19. $2056 \div 41 = 50$ r6
20. $1910 \div 65 = 29$ r25

Exercise 4.17

1. 162 days
2. 51 days
3. 12 complete revolutions
4. 12 stones 11 pounds
5. 92m
6. £49
7. 443 men. No, it is not exact because we used the average weight of a man.

Exercise 4.18: Extension questions – number patterns

1. 0

2. 2 = 2

   2 + 2 = 4

   2 + 2 + 2 = 6

   The numbers produced are even numbers.

3. **(a)** If you multiply an even number by an even number, you always get an even number.

   (b) If you multiply an even number by an odd number, you always get an even number.

   (c) If you multiply an odd number by an even number, you always get an even number.

   (d) If you multiply an odd number by an odd number, you always get an odd number.

4. No.

5. **(a)** If you add an even number to an even number, you get an even number.

   (b) If you add an even number to an odd number, you get an odd number.

   (c) If you add an odd number to an even number, you get an odd number.

   (d) If you add an odd number to an odd number, you get an even number.

6. **(a)** 2, 4, 8, 16, 32, 64   × rule (× 2)

   (b) 1, 5, 25, 125, 625   × rule (× 5)

   (c) 1, 2, 4, 7, 11, 16   + rule (+ 1 more than previous number added)

   (d) 2, 5, 8, 11, 14, 17   + rule (+ 3)

   (e) 11, 101, 1001, 10 001, 100 001   Neither.

Exercise 4.19: Summary exercise

1. (a) $30 \times 10 = 300$ (b) $500 \times 100 = 50\ 000$ (c) $60 \times 1000 = 60\ 000$

2. (a) $400 \div 10 = 40$ (b) $60\ 000 \div 100 = 600$ (c) $7\ 000\ 000 \div 1000 = 7\ 000$

3. (a) $30 \times 600 = 18\ 000$ (b) $500 \times 20 = 10\ 000$ (c) $6000 \times 50 = 300\ 000$

4. (a) $3600 \div 60 = 60 = 60$ (b) $18\ 000 \div 300 = 60$ (c) $720\ 000 \div 80 = 9\ 000$

5. (a) $63 \times 48 \approx 60 \times 50 = 3\ 000$
    (b) $48 \times 32 \times 52 \approx 50 \times 30 \times 50 = 75\ 000$
    (c) $43 \times 69 \times 71 \approx 40 \times 70 \times 70 = 196\ 000$

6. (a) $60\ 000 = 6 \times 10^4$ (b) $300 = 3 \times 10^2$ (c) $400\ 000 = 4 \times 10^5$

7. 6 minibuses   8. 27 days   9. £23 460

10. 129 600 miles   11. 52 631 578 947 368 421   12. £1 176; 20 computers

13. No. $1 \times 21 \times 22 \times 23 = 10\ 626$

14. Total cost is £5,450. Each child £155.72.

End of chapter 4 activities

Rudolph's dilemma

No. of Houses	No. of Ways
2	1
3	2
4	3
5	5
6	8

To find number of ways for 7 houses, add $5 + 8 = 13$

Sequence for the number of ways is: 1, 1, 2, 3, 5, 8, 13, 21, 34, 55, 89, 144, 233, 377, 360

There are 610 ways that Rudolph could travel down Acacia Avenue with its 15 houses.

The Fibonacci sequence

The sum of the rows are the cube numbers:

$1 = 1^3$
$8 = 2^3$
$27 = 3^3$
$64 = 4^3$
$125 = 5^3$

Chapter 5: More about numbers

Exercise 5.1

1. **(a)** yes   **(b)** yes   **(c)** yes   **(d)** yes   **(e)** no

2. **(a)** no   **(b)** yes   **(c)** no   **(d)** yes   **(e)** no

3. **(a)** yes   **(b)** no   **(c)** no   **(d)** no   **(e)** yes

4. 1, 2, 3, 4, 5, 6, 7, 9, 10, 12, 14, 15, 18, 20, 21, 28, 30, 35, 36, 42, 45, 60, 63, 70, 84, 90, 105, 126, 140, 180, 210, 252, 315, 420, 630, 1260

5. **(a)** yes   **(b)** yes   **(c)** yes   **(d)** yes

6. 4

7. 35

8. 24

9. **(a)** 4, 8, 12, 16, 20, 24, 28, 32, $\boxed{36}$ 40, 44, 48, 52, 56, 60
    (b) 6, 12, 18, 24, 30, $\boxed{36}$ 42, 48, 54, 60, 66, 72, 78, 84, 90
    (c) 9, 18, 27, $\boxed{36}$ 45, 54, 63, 72, 81, 90
    (d) 12, 24, $\boxed{36}$ 48, 60, 72, 84, 96, 108, 120

10. **(a)** 1, 7   **(b)** 1, 11   **(c)** 1, 13
    (d) 1, 23   **(e)** 1, 83

    They have only 2 factors: 1 and the number itself.

Exercise 5.2

1. $2 = 2$ $= 2$
    $2^2 = 2 \times 2$ $= 4$
    $2^3 = 2 \times 2 \times 2$ $= 8$
    $2^4 = 2 \times 2 \times 2 \times 2$ $= 16$

2. **(a)** $3 \times 3 \times 3 = 3^3 = 27$ **(d)** $3 \times 3 \times 3 \times 3 \times 3 = 3^5 = 243$
    (b) $4 \times 4 = 4^2 = 16$ **(e)** $7 \times 7 = 7^2 = 49$
    (c) $5 \times 5 \times 5 \times 5 = 5^4 = 625$ **(f)** $6 \times 6 \times 6 = 6^3 = 216$

3. **(a)** $4^3 = 4 \times 4 \times 4 \times 4 = 64$ **(d)** $4^2 = 4 \times 4 = 16$
    (b) $3^4 = 3 \times 3 \times 3 \times 3 = 81$ **(e)** $4^4 = 4 \times 4 \times 4 \times 4 = 256$
    (c) $5^3 = 5 \times 5 \times 5 = 125$ **(f)** $3^3 = 3 \times 3 \times 3 = 27$

4. **(a)** $2^2 + 3^3$
$= (2 \times 2) + (3 \times 3 \times 3)$
$= 4 + 27$
$= 31$

(d) $3^3 + 4^2$
$= (3 \times 3 \times 3) + (4 \times 4)$
$= 27 + 16$
$= 43$

(b) $2^3 - 3^3$
$= (2 \times 2 \times 2) - (3 \times 3 \times 3)$
$= 8 - 27$
$= -19$

(e) $6^3 + 4^2$
$= (6 \times 6 \times 6) + (4 \times 4)$
$= 216 + 16$
$= 232$

(c) $4^3 - 4^3$
$= (4 \times 4 \times 4) - (4 \times 4 \times 4)$
$= 64 - 64$
$= 0$

(f) $5^3 + 5^3$
$= (5 \times 5 \times 5) + (5 \times 5 \times 5)$
$= 125 + 125$
$= 250$

5. **(a)** $4^2 + 3^3$
$= (4 \times 4) + (3 \times 3 \times 3)$
$= 16 + 27$
$= 43$

(d) $3^3 - 4^2$
$= (3 \times 3 \times 3) - (4 \times 4)$
$= 27 - 16$
$= 11$

(b) $5^2 - 2^3$
$= (5 \times 5) - (2 \times 2 \times 2)$
$= 25 - 8$
$= 17$

(e) $5^3 + 3^2$
$= (5 \times 5 \times 5) + (3 \times 3)$
$= 125 + 9$
$= 134$

(c) $5^3 - 4^3$
$= (5 \times 5 \times 5) - (4 \times 4 \times 4)$
$= 125 - 64$
$= 61$

(f) $5^3 + 4^3$
$= (5 \times 5 \times 5) + (4 \times 4 \times 4)$
$= 125 + 64$
$= 189$

Exercise 5.3

1.

Number of dots:
$1 \times 1 = 1$ $\qquad$ $2 \times 2 = 4$ $\qquad$ $3 \times 3 = 9$ $\qquad$ $4 \times 4 = 16$

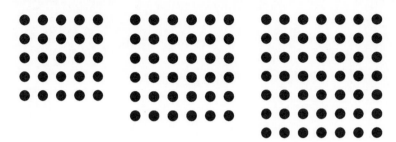

$$5 \times 5 = 25 \qquad 6 \times 6 = 36 \qquad 7 \times 7 = 49$$

2.

  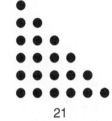

Number of dots:

| 1 | 3 | 6 | 10 | 15 | 21 |

3.

$$
\begin{aligned}
1 &= 1 \\
1 + 2 &= 3 \\
1 + 2 + 3 &= 6 \\
1 + 2 + 3 + 4 &= 10 \\
1 + 2 + 3 + 4 + 5 &= 15 \\
1 + 2 + 3 + 4 + 5 + 6 &= 21 \\
1 + 2 + 3 + 4 + 5 + 6 + 7 &= 28
\end{aligned}
$$

4.

Number of dots:

| 1 = 1 | 3 + 1 = 4 | 6 + 3 = 9 | 10 + 6 = 16 |

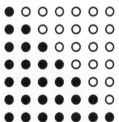

$$15 + 10 = 25 \qquad 21 + 15 = 36 \qquad 28 + 21 = 49$$

5.

1	= 1
1 + 3	= 4
1 + 3 + 5	= 9
1 + 3 + 5 + 7	= 16
1 + 3 + 5 + 7 + 9	= 25
1 + 3 + 5 + 7 + 9 + 11	= 36
1 + 3 + 5 + 7 + 9 + 11 + 13	= 49

6.

2	= 2
2 + 4	= 6
2 + 4 + 6	= 12
2 + 4 + 6 + 8	= 20
2 + 4 + 6 + 8 + 10	= 30
2 + 4 + 6 + 8 + 10 + 12	= 42
2 + 4 + 6 + 8 + 10 + 12 + 14	= 56

The pattern is twice the triangle numbers.

Exercise 5.4

1.

×	2	3	4	5	6	7	8	9	10	11	12
2	4	6	8	10	12	14	16	18	20	22	24
3	6	9	12	15	18	21	24	27	30	33	36
4	8	12	16	20	24	28	32	36	40	44	48
5	10	15	20	25	30	35	40	45	50	55	60
6	12	18	24	30	36	42	48	54	60	66	72
7	14	21	28	35	42	49	56	63	70	77	84
8	16	24	32	40	48	56	64	72	80	88	96
9	18	27	36	45	54	63	72	81	90	99	108
10	20	30	40	50	60	70	80	90	100	110	120
11	22	33	44	55	66	77	88	99	110	121	132
12	24	36	48	60	72	84	96	108	120	132	144

2. Check the diagram. The square numbers in a diagonal forms a line of symmetry.

3. (a) The table square is **symmetrical** about one diagonal.

   (b) All the numbers down that diagonal occur an **odd** number of times.
   They are square numbers.

   (c) The numbers that occur most often are: **24**, **36**, and **48**.
   These numbers have lots of **factors**.

   (d) Some numbers do not occur on the table square at all. These numbers have as factors only 1
   and the number itself. Examples of these are **13**, **23** and **29**. Answers may vary.

Exercise 5.5 : The sieve of Eratosthenes

1.

1	2	3	4	5	6	7	8	9	10
11	12	13	14	15	16	17	18	19	20
21	22	23	24	25	26	27	28	29	30
31	32	33	34	35	36	37	38	39	40
41	42	43	44	45	46	47	48	49	50
51	52	53	54	55	56	57	58	59	60
61	62	63	64	65	66	67	68	69	70
71	72	73	74	75	76	77	78	79	80
81	82	83	84	85	86	87	88	89	90
91	92	93	94	95	96	97	98	99	100

2. 2, 3, 5, 7, 11, 13, 17, 19, 23, 29, 31, 37, 41, 43, 47, 53, 59, 61, 67, 71, 73, 79, 83, 89 and 97.

Exercise 5.6

1.
$1 \times 12 = 12$
$2 \times 6 = 12$
$3 \times 4 = 12$
No

2.
$1 \times 36 = 36$
$2 \times 18 = 36$
$3 \times 12 = 36$
$4 \times 9 = 36$
$6 \times 6 = 36$
Factors of 36 = {1, 2, 3, 4, 6, 9, 12, 18, 36}

3.
$1 \times 72 = 72$
$2 \times 36 = 72$
$3 \times 24 = 72$
$4 \times 18 = 72$
$6 \times 12 = 72$
$8 \times 9 = 72$

4.
$1 \times 100 = 100$
$2 \times 50 = 100$
$4 \times 25 = 100$
$5 \times 20 = 100$
$10 \times 10 = 100$

5. $1 \times 360 = 360$

$2 \times 180 = 360$

$3 \times 120 = 360$

$4 \times 90 = 360$

$5 \times 72 = 360$

$6 \times 60 = 360$

$8 \times 45 = 360$

$9 \times 40 = 360$

$10 \times 36 = 360$

$12 \times 30 = 360$

$15 \times 24 = 360$

$18 \times 20 = 360$

6.   1, 2, 4, 8, 16, 32, 64, 128. The numbers can be generated by doubling.

7.   1, 3, 9, 27, 81, 243. The numbers can be generated by trebling.

8.   **(a)** 4: 1, 2, 4   **(b)** 9: 1, 3, 9   **(c)** 16: 1, 2, 4, 8, 16

(d) 25: 1, 5, 25   **(e)** 36: 1, 2, 3, 4, 6, 9, 12, 18, 36

(f) 49: 1, 7, 49

They all have an odd number of factors.

9.   **(a)** 24, 72 and 360 have an **even** number of factors.

(b) 36 and 100 have an **odd** number of factors. This is because they are **square** numbers.

(c) 360 can be a more useful number than 100 because it has more **factors**.

Exercise 5.7

1. $36 = 2^2 \times 3^2$ **6** $45 = 3^2 \times 5$

2. $25 = 5^2$ **7.** $28 = 2^2 \times 7$

3. $18 = 2 \times 3^2$ **8.** $32 = 2^5$

4. $27 = 3^3$ **9.** $44 = 2^2 \times 11$

5. $40 = 2^3 \times 5$ **10.** $42 = 2 \times 3 \times 7$

Exercise 5.8

1.   **(a)** $36 = 2^2 \times 3^2$ **(d)** $65 = 5 \times 13$ **(g)** $400 = 2^4 \times 5^2$ **(j)** $230 = 2 \times 5 \times 23$

(b) $49 = 7^2$ **(e)** $72 = 2^3 \times 3^2$ **(h)** $162 = 2 \times 3^4$ **(k)** $360 = 2^3 \times 3^2 \times 5$

(c) $56 = 2^3 \times 7$ **(f)** $125 = 5^3$ **(i)** $144 = 2^4 \times 3^2$ **(l)** $365 = 5 \times 73$

2.   **(a)** $24 = 2^3 \times 3$; $54 = 2 \times 3^3$

        (b) 2 and 3

3. $125 = 5^3$; $100 = 2^2 \times 5^2$;   common prime factor is 5.

4. $12 = 2^2 \times 3$; $30 = 2 \times 3 \times 5$; $48 = 2^4 \times 3$; common prime factors are 2 and 3.

5.   **(a)** $2 \times 2 \times 2 \times 3 \times 3 \times 3$ Pupils may write 2, 2, **2, 3** and **2, 3**, 3, 3

        (b) $2^3 \times 3^3 = 216$; $216 \div 24 = 9$; $216 \div 54 = 4$; yes

        (c) No

6.   **(a)** $2 \times 2 \times 5 \times 5 \times 5$

           $2^2 \times 5^3 = 500$; $500 \div 125 = 4$; $500 \div 100 = 5$; yes

           No

        (b) $2 \times 2 \times 2 \times 2 \times 3 \times 5$

           $2^4 \times 3 \times 5 = 240$; $240 \div 12 = 20$; $240 \div 30 = 8$; $240 \div 48 = 5$

           No

7.   30, 60, 90

        They have 3 or 4 prime factors.

8.   360 and 480 both have 24. They both have 3 different prime factors (2, 3 and 5)

9.   30, 60 and 90 have 3 (2, 3, 5); 70 has 3 (2, 5, 7); 42 and 84 have 3 (2, 3, 7); All have 8 factors.

10.   210 has 4 different prime factors, 16 factors in all (1, 2, 3, 5, 6, 7, 10, 14, 15, 21, 30, 35, 42, 70, 105 and 210).

Exercise 5.9

1.   **(a)** 3   **(e)** 6   **(i)** 2

        (b) 4   **(f)** 5   **(j)** 8

        (c) 20   **(g)** 18   **(k)** 3

        (d) 6   **(h)** 10   **(l)** 4

2.   12 eggs

3.   The brother is 18 years old. He is 2 or 6, most likely 6 years old.

Exercise 5.10

1.   **(a)** 36   **(e)** 30   **(i)** 24

        (b) 126   **(f)** 28   **(j)** 72

        (c) 400   **(g)** 200   **(k)** 150

        (d) 180   **(h)** 90   **(l)** 1680

2.   75 seconds

3.   24th lily pad. No, the prince has to make 3 jumps, the princess has to make 4.

Exercise 5.11

1.	10	**5.**	11	**9.**	8	**13.**	35
2.	1	**6.**	6	**10.**	20	**14.**	45
3.	5	**7.**	7	**11.**	12	**15.**	30
4.	12	**8.**	9	**12.**	21	**16.**	36

Exercise 5.12: Summary exercise

1. **(a)** 225; yes   **(c)** 134; no   **(e)** 143; no

   (b) 132; yes   **(d)** 1023; yes   **(f)** 6000; yes

2. **(a)** 225 and 6000   **(b)** 132 and 6000   **(c)** 225

3. **(a)** 1, 2, 4, 8, 16

   (b) 1, 2, 4, 7, 14, 28

   (c) 1, 2, 4, 5, 8, 10, 20, 40

   (d) 1, 2, 5, 10, 25, 50

4.
   $1 \times 120 \quad = 120$
   $2 \times 60 \quad = 120$
   $3 \times 40 \quad = 120$
   $4 \times 30 \quad = 120$
   $5 \times 24 \quad = 120$
   $6 \times 20 \quad = 120$
   $8 \times 15 \quad = 120$
   $10 \times 12 \quad = 120$

5. **(a)** 100   **(f)** 70

   (b) 14   **(g)** 2, 4, 8, ... powers of 2.

   (c) 91   **(h)** 1, 3, 5, 7, 9 ... all odd numbers

   (d) 98   **(i)** 100 (or 50 if you do not include 500)

   (e) 19

6. **(a)** 5×7 **(b)** 3×7 **(c)** $2^4 \times 3^2$ **(d)** $2^2 \times 3 \times 13$

7. **(a)** HCF 3; LCM 360   **(b)** HCF 2; LCM 336

8. 120 seconds

End of chapter activity: A one to a hundred square investigation

It is true of all 3 × 3 squares. If you double the number in the middle it is the same as the sum of the opposite corners or opposite centres.

1. **(a)** Check pupils' drawings.

    (b) Check pupils' answers, the sums of the opposite corners should be equal.

    (c) Check pupils' answers, the sums of the centre of opposite sides should be equal.

    (d) The answer should be the same as the anwer to (b) and (c) above.

2. Check pupils' answers given for 3 × 3 squares.

    Things to notice about 4 × 4 squares:

    The sums of opposite corners are equal.

    The sums of opposite central numbers are equal;

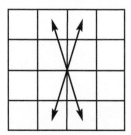 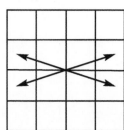

and equal to sum of centres like this.

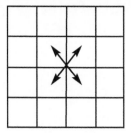

Chapter 6: Symmetry

Exercise 6.1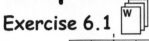

1.

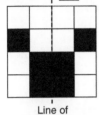

Line of symmetry

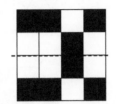 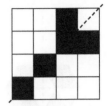

2.

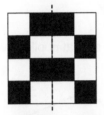 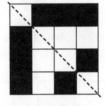 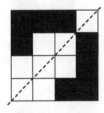

3.

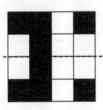 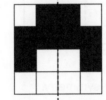 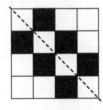 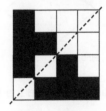

4.

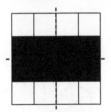  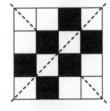 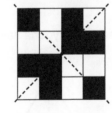

5.

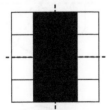 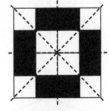 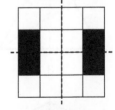

6.

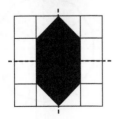 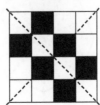 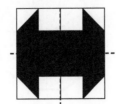 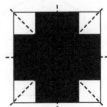

7.

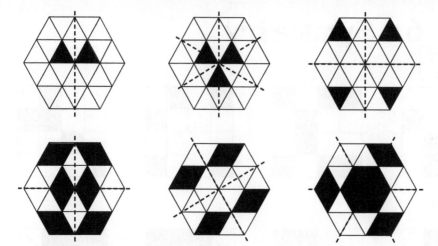

8.

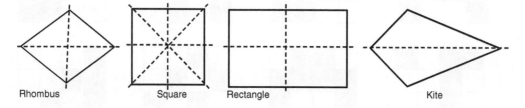

9. Teachers might wish to hand out 2 copies of the worksheet for this question, so that pupils have one to experiment with and one to mark up the answers.

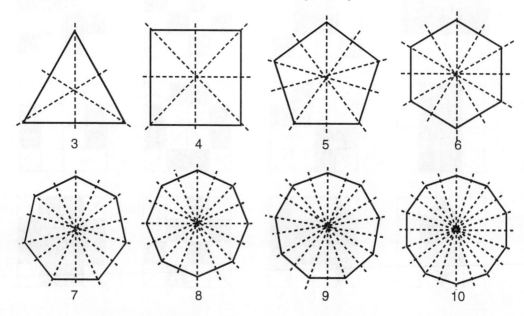

Rhombus   Square   Rectangle   Kite

The parallelogram and the trapezium have no lines of symmetry.

10. All the regular polygons have the same number of lines of symmetry as the number of sides.

3   4   5   6

7   8   9   10

11.

Exercise 6.2

1. A square has an order of rotational symmetry of 4. Rectangle, rhombus, parallelogram have a rotational symmetry of 2.

2. Same order of rotational symmetry as number of sides.

3.

	Rotational Symmetry	Order of Rotational Symmetry		Rotational Symmetry	Order of Rotational Symmetry
	Yes No	3	STOP	Yes No	. . . .
	Yes No	. . . .		Yes No	2
	Yes No	. . . .		Yes No	2
	Yes No	. . . .		Yes No	. . . .
	Yes No	. . . .		Yes No	. . . .
	Yes No	. . . .		Yes No	. . . .
	Yes No	. . . .		Yes No	. . . .
	Yes No	. . . .		Yes No	. . . .

4. Check pupils' own designs for:

    (a) DANGER!   (d) Bridge

    (b) Restaurant   (e) Ball games prohibited

    (c) Cinema   (f) Hotel

Exercise 6.3

1.

(a) 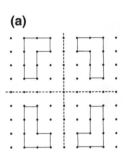 (b) 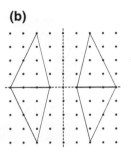 (c) 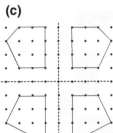 (d)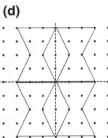

2.

(a) 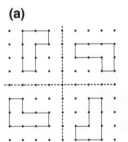 (b) 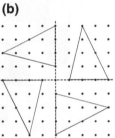 (c) 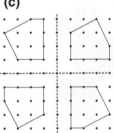 (d)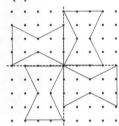

3. There is more than one possible answer, examples are:

(a) 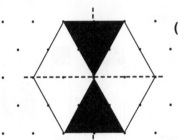 (b)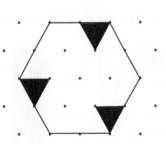

(c) 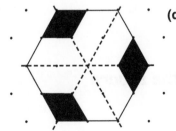 (d)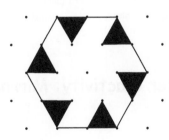

Exercise 6.4: Summary exercise

1.

(a)

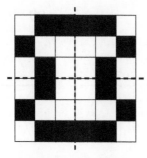 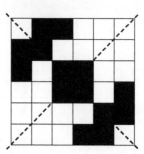

(b)

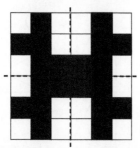 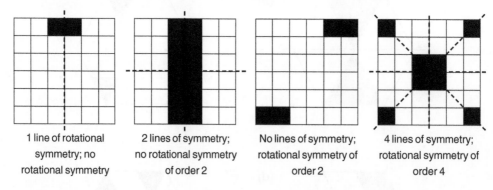

2.   Square, rectangle, rhombus

3.   Parallelogram, order 2 but no lines of symmetry.

4.   There is more than one possible answer, examples are:

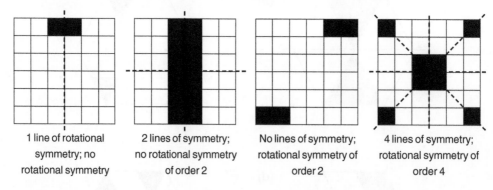

| 1 line of rotational symmetry; no rotational symmetry | 2 lines of symmetry; no rotational symmetry of order 2 | No lines of symmetry; rotational symmetry of order 2 | 4 lines of symmetry; rotational symmetry of order 4 |

End of chapter 6 activity: Mirror on the square

Practical

Chapter 7: Introducing fractions

Exercise 7.1

1. $\frac{1}{4}$

2. $\frac{1}{4}$

3. 30 minutes, 15 minutes

4. $\frac{1}{2}$

5. $\frac{1}{4}$ chocolate cake, $\frac{3}{16}$ strawberry cake

6. $\frac{1}{8}$

7. William

8. Neither, they both have 6 pieces

9. $\frac{1}{3}$

10. $\frac{1}{3}$

Exercise 7.2

1. (a) Shade half   (b) Shade 1 block   (c) Shade 2 blocks   (d) Shade 8 blocks

Note: Check pupils have coloured one half of the rectangle. There is more than one posibility.

2. (a) Shade $\frac{1}{2}$ of 1 block   (b) Shade 1 block   (c) Shade 1 block   (d) Shade 4 blocks

Note: Check pupils have coloured one quarter of the rectangle. There is more than one posibility.

3. (a) $\frac{1}{4}$ (b) $\frac{1}{3}$ (c) $\frac{2}{3}$ (d) $\frac{1}{2}$

4. (a) $\frac{1}{6}$ (c) $\frac{1}{4}$ (e) $\frac{1}{2}$
   (b) $\frac{1}{2}$ (d) $\frac{1}{2}$ (f) $\frac{7}{24}$

5. (a) (b) (c) (d) check pupils' drawings.

6. (a) $\frac{7}{12}$ (b) $\frac{2}{3}$ (c) $\frac{6}{23}$ (d) $\frac{3}{11}$ (e) $\frac{17}{25}$

7. (b) $\frac{24}{35}$ and (d) $\frac{8}{25}$ are correct.

8. (a) $\frac{1}{3} = \frac{4}{12} = \frac{8}{24} = \frac{33}{99}$ (c) $\frac{1}{4} = \frac{3}{12} = \frac{6}{24} = \frac{12}{48}$
   (b) $\frac{3}{5} = \frac{9}{15} = \frac{15}{25} = \frac{33}{55}$ (d) $\frac{2}{9} = \frac{4}{18} = \frac{6}{27} = \frac{50}{225}$

Exercise 7.3

1. (a) 6   (b) 63   (c) 8   (d) 24   (e) 15   (f) 12

2. (a) $\frac{3}{6}, \frac{4}{6}$ $\frac{2}{3} > \frac{1}{2}$ (c) $\frac{2}{8}, \frac{3}{8}$ $\frac{3}{8} > \frac{1}{4}$ (e) $\frac{6}{15}, \frac{10}{15}$ $\frac{2}{3} > \frac{2}{5}$

    (b) $\frac{27}{63}, \frac{28}{63}$ $\frac{4}{9} > \frac{3}{7}$ (d) $\frac{21}{24}, \frac{20}{24}$ $\frac{7}{8} > \frac{5}{6}$ (f) $\frac{7}{12}, \frac{8}{12}$ $\frac{2}{3} > \frac{7}{12}$

3. (a) $\frac{3}{5}$ (b) $\frac{5}{12}$ (c) $\frac{1}{3}$ (d) $\frac{5}{9}$ (e) $\frac{2}{15}$ (f) $\frac{2}{3}$

4. $\frac{3}{7}$ $\frac{4}{9}$ $\frac{1}{2}$ $\frac{2}{3}$

5. $\frac{4}{9}$ $\frac{1}{3}$ $\frac{2}{15}$ $\frac{1}{12}$

6. (a) $\frac{5}{9}$ (b) $\frac{22}{36}$ (c) $\frac{3}{9}$ (d) $\frac{4}{15}$

Exercise 7.4

1. (a) $\frac{7}{4}$ (c) $\frac{17}{5}$ (e) $\frac{15}{7}$ (g) $\frac{34}{5}$ (i) $\frac{103}{10}$ (k) $\frac{76}{9}$

    (b) $\frac{52}{7}$ (d) $\frac{62}{5}$ (f) $\frac{55}{12}$ (h) $\frac{63}{4}$ (j) $\frac{82}{9}$ (l) $\frac{65}{12}$

2. (a) $3\frac{1}{4}$ (c) $3\frac{1}{2}$ (e) $2\frac{1}{9}$ (g) 6   (i) $7\frac{3}{4}$ (k) $7\frac{7}{11}$

    (b) $2\frac{7}{8}$ (d) $2\frac{9}{10}$ (f) $13\frac{1}{2}$ (h) $6\frac{1}{4}$ (j) $20\frac{1}{5}$ (l) 5

Exercise 7.5

1. 8   6. 4
2. 5   7. 2
3. 5   8. 2
4. 4   9. 4
5. 3   10. 3

Exercise 7.6

1. 18   6. 8
2. 25   7. 8   11. $\frac{1}{3}$ of 21
3. 6   8. 12   12. $\frac{3}{4}$ of 16
4. 6   9. 15   13. $\frac{2}{3}$ of 24
5. 20   10. 21   14. Neither, they are the same.

Exercise 7.7

1. $\frac{1}{2}$ 4. $\frac{1}{4}$ 7. $\frac{1}{2}$ 10. $1\frac{1}{2}$ 13. $1\frac{1}{2}$ 16. $1\frac{2}{3}$

2. $\frac{2}{5}$ 5. $\frac{4}{9}$ 8. 1 11. $1\frac{3}{5}$ 14. $1\frac{1}{3}$ 17. $1\frac{2}{5}$

3. $\frac{2}{3}$ 6. $\frac{5}{8}$ 9. $\frac{1}{2}$ 12. $1\frac{1}{3}$ 15. $1\frac{1}{4}$ 18. $1\frac{1}{2}$

Exercise 7.8

1. $4\frac{1}{2}$ 4. 6 7. 5

2. 3 5. $3\frac{1}{9}$ 8. $5\frac{2}{5}$

3. $4\frac{1}{3}$ 6. $2\frac{7}{8}$ 9. $5\frac{1}{5}$

Exercise 7.9

1. $\frac{1}{2}$ 4. $\frac{3}{4}$ 7. $\frac{2}{7}$ 10. $1\frac{1}{2}$ 13. $1\frac{3}{4}$ 16. $1\frac{1}{3}$

2. $\frac{3}{5}$ 5. $\frac{5}{9}$ 8. $\frac{2}{3}$ 11. $2\frac{1}{5}$ 14. $\frac{2}{3}$ 17. $\frac{4}{5}$

3. $\frac{2}{3}$ 6. $\frac{1}{2}$ 9. $\frac{3}{5}$ 12. $\frac{2}{3}$ 15. $2\frac{1}{2}$ 18. $2\frac{3}{5}$

Exercise 7.10

1. $1\frac{1}{2}$ 4. $1\frac{3}{4}$ 7. $2\frac{1}{3}$ 10. 4 13. $\frac{1}{2}$ 16. $\frac{5}{9}$

2. $3\frac{3}{5}$ 5. $2\frac{8}{9}$ 8. $3\frac{4}{5}$ 11. $1\frac{3}{5}$ 14. $1\frac{4}{9}$ 17. $4\frac{1}{2}$

3. $\frac{2}{3}$ 6. $2\frac{3}{4}$ 9. $2\frac{3}{5}$ 12. $7\frac{1}{5}$ 15. $3\frac{1}{4}$ 18. $\frac{4}{5}$

Exercise 7.11

1. $1\frac{3}{4}$ 4. $1\frac{7}{8}$ 7. $2\frac{5}{8}$ 10. $4\frac{1}{4}$ 13. $5\frac{1}{8}$ 16. $5\frac{7}{8}$

2. $\frac{1}{2}$ 5. $\frac{4}{9}$ 8. $2\frac{1}{6}$ 11. $5\frac{1}{10}$ 14. $2\frac{7}{9}$ 17. $4\frac{1}{2}$

3. $\frac{1}{2}$ 6. $\frac{8}{9}$ 9. $1\frac{4}{5}$ 12. $1\frac{1}{2}$ 15. $5\frac{4}{9}$ 18. $4\frac{1}{2}$

Exercise 7.12

1. $\frac{13}{20}$

2. $\frac{26}{35}$

3. $\frac{13}{15}$

4. $\frac{19}{24}$

5. $\frac{26}{45}$

6. $\frac{27}{40}$

7. $1\frac{7}{12}$

8. $1\frac{11}{35}$

9. $1\frac{7}{20}$

Exercise 7.13

1. $4\frac{13}{15}$

2. $5\frac{26}{35}$

3. $5\frac{21}{40}$

4. $8\frac{23}{40}$

5. $5\frac{3}{35}$

6. $10\frac{7}{12}$

7. $4\frac{7}{15}$

8. $7\frac{7}{12}$

9. $8\frac{3}{4}$

10. $9\frac{16}{45}$

11. $6\frac{37}{40}$

12. $11\frac{47}{60}$

Exercise 7.14

1. $\frac{2}{15}$

2. $\frac{5}{12}$

3. $\frac{11}{24}$

4. $\frac{8}{21}$

5. $\frac{1}{24}$

6. $\frac{7}{15}$

7. $\frac{8}{45}$

8. $\frac{1}{9}$

9. $\frac{1}{21}$

Exercise 7.15

1. $2\frac{7}{15}$

2. $1\frac{7}{15}$

3. $2\frac{5}{24}$

4. $1\frac{1}{21}$

5. $1\frac{11}{24}$

6. $1\frac{4}{15}$

7. $1\frac{11}{45}$

8. $1\frac{1}{9}$

9. $2\frac{6}{35}$

Exercise 7.16

1. $1\frac{13}{15}$

2. $2\frac{7}{12}$

3. $1\frac{11}{24}$

4. $2\frac{11}{24}$

5. $3\frac{2}{3}$

6. $1\frac{6}{35}$

7. $2\frac{5}{12}$

8. $\frac{11}{15}$

9. $2\frac{39}{40}$

10. $\frac{8}{15}$

11. $1\frac{7}{8}$

12. $2\frac{22}{35}$

13. $\frac{11}{24}$

14. $1\frac{13}{21}$

15. $\frac{5}{12}$

16. $1\frac{5}{18}$

17. $\frac{15}{28}$

18. $3\frac{13}{24}$

Exercise 7.17

1. $\dfrac{2}{3}$

2. $\dfrac{1}{6}$

3. $4\dfrac{3}{4}$

4. $14\dfrac{1}{4}$

5. $\dfrac{5}{12}$

6. $2\dfrac{3}{5}$

7. $\dfrac{3}{20}$

8. $\dfrac{1}{12}$

9. 11:45

10. $\dfrac{1}{2}$

Exercise 7.18: Extension questions

1. $\dfrac{1}{2} = \dfrac{1}{2}$

$\dfrac{1}{2} + \dfrac{2}{3} = \dfrac{7}{6} = 1\dfrac{1}{6}$

$\dfrac{1}{2} + \dfrac{2}{3} + \dfrac{3}{4} = \dfrac{23}{12} = 1\dfrac{11}{12}$

$\dfrac{1}{2} + \dfrac{2}{3} + \dfrac{3}{4} + \dfrac{4}{5} = \dfrac{173}{60} = 2\dfrac{43}{60}$

$\dfrac{1}{2} + \dfrac{2}{3} + \dfrac{3}{4} + \dfrac{4}{5} + \dfrac{5}{6} = \dfrac{223}{60} = 3\dfrac{11}{20}$

$\dfrac{1}{2} + \dfrac{2}{3} + \dfrac{3}{4} + \dfrac{4}{5} + \dfrac{5}{6} + \dfrac{6}{7} = \dfrac{3111}{420} = 4\dfrac{57}{140}$

2. $\dfrac{1}{3} = \dfrac{1}{3}$

$\dfrac{1}{3} + \dfrac{3}{5} = \dfrac{14}{15}$

$\dfrac{1}{3} + \dfrac{3}{5} + \dfrac{5}{7} = \dfrac{175}{105} = 1\dfrac{68}{105}$

$\dfrac{1}{3} + \dfrac{3}{5} + \dfrac{5}{7} + \dfrac{7}{9} = \dfrac{2292}{945} = 2\dfrac{134}{315}$

$\dfrac{1}{3} + \dfrac{3}{5} + \dfrac{5}{7} + \dfrac{7}{9} + \dfrac{9}{11} = \dfrac{33717}{10395} = 3\dfrac{844}{3465}$

$\dfrac{1}{3} + \dfrac{3}{5} + \dfrac{5}{7} + \dfrac{7}{9} + \dfrac{9}{11} + \dfrac{11}{13} = \dfrac{552666}{135135} = 4\dfrac{4042}{45045}$

3. $\dfrac{1}{2} = \dfrac{1}{2}$

$\dfrac{1}{2} + \dfrac{1}{4} = \dfrac{3}{4}$

$\dfrac{1}{2} + \dfrac{1}{4} + \dfrac{1}{8} = \dfrac{7}{8}$

$\dfrac{1}{2} + \dfrac{1}{4} + \dfrac{1}{8} + \dfrac{1}{16} = \dfrac{15}{16}$

$\dfrac{1}{2} + \dfrac{1}{4} + \dfrac{1}{8} + \dfrac{1}{16} + \dfrac{1}{32} = \dfrac{31}{32}$

$\dfrac{1}{2} + \dfrac{1}{4} + \dfrac{1}{8} + \dfrac{1}{16} + \dfrac{1}{32} + \dfrac{1}{64} = \dfrac{63}{64}$

The sum will never quite equal one, it will get closer and closer to one.

Is there a point when the answer is so close to one that you can assume that it is equal to one? (For discussion.)

4. $\dfrac{1}{10} = \dfrac{1}{10}$

$\dfrac{1}{10} + \dfrac{1}{100} = \dfrac{11}{100}$

$\dfrac{1}{10} + \dfrac{1}{100} + \dfrac{1}{1000} = \dfrac{111}{1000}$

No, you will never get $\dfrac{2}{10}$ or $\dfrac{1}{5}$

Exercise 7.19: Summary exercise

1. $\dfrac{1}{4}$

2. 24

3. (a) $\dfrac{6}{13}$ (b) $\dfrac{7}{10}$ (c) $\dfrac{4}{3} = 1\dfrac{1}{3}$ (d) $\dfrac{5}{4} = 1\dfrac{1}{4}$

4. $\dfrac{3}{4} = \dfrac{9}{12} = \dfrac{18}{24} = \dfrac{24}{32} = \dfrac{90}{120}$

5. $\dfrac{7}{9}$

6. $\dfrac{4}{5}$ or any fraction between $\dfrac{3}{4}$ and $\dfrac{5}{6}$

7. (a) $\dfrac{17}{20}$ (b) $1\dfrac{5}{12}$ (c) $4\dfrac{11}{18}$ (d) $4\dfrac{13}{40}$

8. (a) $\dfrac{5}{28}$ (b) $\dfrac{1}{24}$ (c) $\dfrac{11}{30}$ (d) $1\dfrac{11}{20}$

9. 0

10. 5 hours 25 minutes. Note this answer is based on the straight foward interpretation of the question, i.e. in the first hour the snail climbs 10 cm but slips 1 cm; by the end of the second hour he has climbed a total of 20 cm and now slips 10% of 20 cm i.e 2 cm; in the third hour he has climbed a total of 30 cm so slips 3cm; and so on until 5 hours later he reaches the top of the bucket.

End of chapter 7 activity: Imperial units

Practical

1.
1 m = 3 ft 3 ins	1 ft = 0.3 m	10 ft = 3.0 m
2 m = 6 ft 6 ins	2 ft = 0.6 m	11 ft = 3.3 m
3 m = 9 ft 9 ins	3 ft = 0.9 m	12 ft = 3.6 m
4 m = 13 ft	4 ft = 1.2 m	13 ft = 3.9 m
5 m = 16 ft 3 ins	5 ft = 1.5 m	14 ft = 4.2 m
	6 ft = 1.8 m	15 ft = 4.5 m
	7 ft = 2.1 m	16 ft = 4.6 m
	8 ft = 2.4 m	
	9 ft = 2.7 m	

Chapter 8: Introducing decimals, money and the metric system

Exercise 8.1

	H T U . $\frac{1}{10}$ $\frac{1}{100}$			H T U . $\frac{1}{10}$ $\frac{1}{100}$
1.	0 . 1		**11.**	4 . 0 2
2.	0 . 0 1		**12.**	6 . 1 2
3.	0 . 4		**13.**	4 0 0 . 2
4.	0 . 0 5		**14.**	4 2 . 3
5.	3 . 1		**15.**	4 0 . 3
6.	0 . 1 4		**16.**	3 0 0 . 0 4
7.	0 . 5		**17.**	4 0 0 . 3 1
8.	0 . 2 5		**18.**	5 0 . 1 6
9.	8 . 4		**19.**	1 2 . 6
10.	0 . 3 5		**20.**	1 6 0 . 1 4

Exercise 8.2

1.	$\frac{2}{5}$	**6.**	$\frac{3}{20}$	**11.**	$3\frac{19}{100}$	**16.**	$3\frac{63}{125}$
2.	$\frac{4}{5}$	**7.**	$\frac{9}{10}$	**12.**	$3\frac{1}{200}$	**17.**	$2\frac{7}{100}$
3.	$\frac{1}{2}$	**8.**	$\frac{3}{50}$	**13.**	$1\frac{113}{125}$	**18.**	$21\frac{1}{200}$
4.	$\frac{1}{25}$	**9.**	$\frac{13}{125}$	**14.**	$2\frac{1}{20}$	**19.**	$4\frac{1}{100}$
5.	$\frac{13}{100}$	**10.**	$\frac{23}{25}$	**15.**	$\frac{8}{25}$	**20.**	$6\frac{57}{100}$

Exercise 8.3

1.	0.7	**6.**	0.003	**11.**	0.6	**16.**	0.035
2.	0.29	**7.**	0.303	**12.**	0.5	**17.**	0.254
3.	0.117	**8.**	0.51	**13.**	0.35	**18.**	0.412
4.	0.02	**9.**	0.29	**14.**	0.54	**19.**	0.18
5.	0.9	**10.**	0.099	**15.**	0.36	**20.**	0.008

Exercise 8.4

1.	0.403	6.	21.23	11.	13.445
2.	1.003	7.	178.1	12.	155.55
3.	40.5	8.	15.32	13.	62.25
4.	700.06	9.	40.53	14.	27.75
5.	40.32	10.	105.96	15.	52.117

Exercise 8.5

1.	22.01	6.	1.15
2.	4.09	7.	1.127
3.	2.72	8.	1.06
4.	17.09	9.	3.366
5.	5.79	10.	20.664

Exercise 8.6

1.	9.8	6.	49.884
2.	2.652	7.	6.9
3.	47.985	8.	27.25
4.	30.75	9.	186.6
5.	45	10.	98.01

Exercise 8.7

1.	£3.64	6.	£3.20	11.	£13.77
2.	£1.25	7.	£3.22	12.	£1.50
3.	36p	8.	£2.54	13.	£9.75
4.	£1.05	9.	£4.10	14.	£30.00
5.	£3.66	10.	(a) £2.70	15.	£13.10
			(b) 55p		

Exercise 8.8

1.	4	6.	3.003
2.	5.5	7.	0.5
3.	60.6	8.	10.7
4.	120	9.	2.33
5.	3.3	10.	1009

11.	0.2	2.02	2.22	20.02	22.02
12.	0.033	0.3	0.303	0.33	3.30
13.	0.3	3.6	6	6.06	6.6
14.	0.12	1.012	1.2	1.22	12
15.	0.03	0.5	3.05	3.5	5.003
16.	0.19	1.9	9	9.01	9.1
17.	0.06	6.006	6.66	60	66.6
18.	0.077	0.77	7.7	77.7	770
19.	0.45	0.504	4.5	5.4	450
20.	0.081	0.18	0.8	1.8	81

Exercise 8.9

1.	410	**6.**	3800	**11.**	2.45
2.	35	**7.**	840	**12.**	0.362
3.	40	**8.**	7200	**13.**	235 000
4.	640	**9.**	40	**14.**	0.126
5.	1	**10.**	36 000	**15.**	0.0125

16.	75 000	**21.**	1005	**26.**	60
17.	0.362	**22.**	0.00305	**27.**	0.05
18.	30.2	**23.**	0.5	**28.**	10 400
19.	1.05	**24.**	30.5	**29.**	0.807
20.	40 000	**25.**	250	**30.**	0.07

Exercise 8.10

1.	**(a)** 2 m	**(c)** 0.4 m	**(e)** 5000 m	**(g)** 0.25 m
	(b) 400 m	**(d)** 35 000 m	**(f)** 3.05 m	**(h)** 0.025 m
2.	**(a)** 20 000 g	**(b)** 3 g	**(c)** 400 g	**(d)** 0.35 g
3.	**(a)** 0.2 l	**(b)** 30 l	**(c)** 0.25 l	**(d)** 0.005 l
4.	**(a)** 20 cm	**(b)** 200 000 cm	**(c)** 30 000 cm	**(d)** 500 cm
5.	**(a)** 3.5 kg	**(b)** 0.04 kg	**(c)** 0.00025 kg	**(d)** 75 kg
6.	**(a)** 10 000 ml	**(b)** 350 000 ml	**(c)** 500 ml	**(d)** 70 ml
7.	**(a)** 320 mm	**(b)** 45 mm	**(c)** 630 mm	**(d)** 4 000 000 mm

8.   **(a)** 320 000 mg   **(b)** 5500 000 mg   **(c)** 1500 mg   **(d)** 500 000 mg

9.   **(a)** 35.6 km   **(b)** 0.455 km   **(c)** 0.32 km   **(d)** 4.5 km

Exercise 8.11

1.   552.5 cm   2.   4.35 l   3.   3.02004 kg   4.   4.5 m (no base!)

5.   4 m   6.   3.8826 kg   7.   £1.64   8.   1.38 l

Exercise 8.12

1.   **(a)** 203.6   **(b)** 203.56   **(c)** 203.561
2.   **(a)** 3.4   **(b)** 3.42   **(c)** 3.419
3.   **(a)** 0.4   **(b)** 0.41   **(c)** 0.405
4.   **(a)** 6.0   **(b)** 6.05   **(c)** 6.047
5.   **(a)** 15.9   **(b)** 15.90   **(c)** 15.903
6.   **(a)** 0.0   **(b)** 0.04   **(c)** 0.040
7.   **(a)** 0.0   **(b)** 0.03   **(c)** 0.031
8.   **(a)** 22.0   **(b)** 22.05   **(c)** 22.046
9.   **(a)** 1.6   **(b)** 1.56   **(c)** 1.556
10.   **(a)** 1.0   **(b)** 1.00   **(c)** 1.000
11.   **(a)** 1.1   **(b)** 1.09   **(c)** 1.091
12.   **(a)** 20.0   **(b)** 20.02   **(c)** 20.021
13.   **(a)** 10.0   **(b)** 10.00   **(c)** 10.000
14.   **(a)** 10.0   **(b)** 10.00   **(c)** 10.000
15.   **(a)** 101.0   **(b)** 101.00   **(c)** 101.000

Exercise 8.13

1.   **(a)** 0.25   **(b)** 0.5   **(c)** 0.75   **(d)** 1.0
2.   **(a)** 0.125   **(b)** 0.375   **(c)** 0.625   **(d)** 0.875
3.   **(a)** 0.2   **(b)** 0.4   **(c)** 0.6   **(d)** 0.8
4.   **(a)** 0.1   **(b)** 0.3   **(c)** 0.5   **(d)** 0.7
5.   **(a)** 0.0625   **(b)** 0.1875   **(c)** 0.3125   **(d)** 0.4375

Exercise 8.14

1. **(a)** $\frac{1}{3} = 0.\dot{3}$, $\frac{2}{3} = 0.\dot{6}$ (one number repeats)

   (b) $\frac{1}{6} = 0.1\dot{6}$, $\frac{2}{6} = 0.\dot{3}$, $\frac{3}{6} = 0.5$, $\frac{4}{6} = 0.\dot{6}$, $\frac{5}{6} = 0.8\dot{3}$, (one number repeats)

   (c) $\frac{1}{9} = 0.\dot{1}$, $\frac{2}{9} = 0.\dot{2}$, $\frac{3}{9} = 0.\dot{3}$, $\frac{4}{9} = 0.\dot{4}$, $\frac{5}{9} = 0.\dot{5}$, $\frac{6}{9} = 0.\dot{6}$, $\frac{7}{9} = 0.\dot{7}$, $\frac{8}{9} = 0.\dot{8}$ (one num repeats)

   (d) $\frac{1}{11} = 0.\dot{0}\dot{9}$, $\frac{2}{11} = 0.\dot{1}\dot{8}$, $\frac{3}{11} = 0.\dot{2}\dot{7}$, $\frac{4}{11} = 0.\dot{3}\dot{6}$, $\frac{5}{11} = 0.\dot{4}\dot{5}$, $\frac{6}{11} = 0.\dot{5}\dot{4}$, $\frac{7}{11} = 0.\dot{6}\dot{3}$

   $\frac{8}{11} = 0.\dot{7}\dot{2}$, $\frac{9}{11} = 0.\dot{8}\dot{1}$, $\frac{10}{11} = 0.\dot{9}\dot{0}$, (two number repeats)

   (e) $\frac{1}{7} = 0.\dot{1}4285\dot{7}$, $\frac{2}{7} = 0.\dot{2}8571\dot{4}$, $\frac{3}{7} = 0.\dot{4}2857\dot{1}$, $\frac{4}{7} = 0.\dot{5}7142\dot{8}$, $\frac{5}{7} = 0.\dot{7}1428\dot{5}$

   $\frac{6}{7} = 0.\dot{8}5714\dot{2}$ (six number repeats)

2. **(a)** They are factors of 10 or 100 or 1000
   (b) They are not factors of 10, 100 or 1000 etc

Exercise 8.15: Extension questions

1. **(a)-(e)** Answers as in 1. above. One number repeats: thirds, sixths, ninths. Two number repeats: elevenths

2. They have recurring 3s or 6s but $\frac{1}{6}$ and $\frac{5}{6}$ have another digit first.

   $\frac{1}{22} = 0.0\dot{4}\dot{5}$ (two repeat numbers)

3. Multiples of 7: $\frac{1}{14} = 0.0\dot{7}1428\dot{5}$; $\frac{1}{21} = 0.\dot{0}4761\dot{9}0$

   Multiples of 9: $\frac{1}{18} = 0.0\dot{5}$; $\frac{1}{27} = 0.\dot{0}3\dot{7}$

   Multiples of 11: $\frac{1}{22} = 0.0\dot{4}\dot{5}$; $\frac{1}{33} = 0.\dot{3}\dot{0}$

4. 2 number repeats: elevenths, thirteens and multiples

   3 number repeats: thirty sevenths ($\frac{1}{37} = 0.\dot{0}2\dot{7}0$) and multiples e.g. $\frac{1}{111}$

   4 number repeats: 'one hundred and oneths' ($\frac{1}{101} = 0.00\dot{9}90\dot{0}9$)

   5 number repeats: 'forty oneths' ($\frac{1}{41} = 0.\dot{0}243\dot{9}$)

   6 number repeats: sevenths

Exercise 8.16: Summary exercise

1. **(a)** 2.5   **(b)** 13.40

2. **(a)** $\frac{3}{5}$ **(b)** $\frac{6}{25}$ **(c)** $1\frac{1}{8}$

3. **(a)** 5.55   **(b)** 113.33

4.   **(a)** 1.75   **(b)** 3.68

5.   35p

6.   **(a)** 2 m   **(b)** 2000 mm   **(c)** 0.002 km

7.   **(a)** 5000 g   **(b)** 5000 000 mg

8.   **(a)** 0.05 l   **(b)** 5 cl

9.   No

10.   **(a)** 15   **(b)** 14.5   **(c)** 14.53   **(d)** 14.527

11.   **(a)** 0.05   0.50   5   5.05   50

      (b) 0.04   0.404   4.004   4.04   40.4

12.   **(a)** £33.79

      (b) 86p

End of chapter activity

Mathematics from food!

1.   Cereal A provides more energy, and contains more sugar and sodium. Cereal B has more protein and fibre.

2.   Fibre is good for digestion, sodium is salt and too much is bad for you.

3.   Cereal B has less sugar and sodium and more fibre.

4.   Cereal A has more sugary things.

5.   Cereal A! We like sugar!

6.   Things from Cereal B, because they are good for you, and things like dried bananas, honey, raisins that are natural sugars to make it taste nice.

Chapter 9: Time, travel and tables

Exercise 9.1

1. 108

2. 27th August

3. **(a)** Thursday   **(d)** Monday
   (b) Tuesday   **(e)** Sunday
   (c) Wednesday   **(f)** Answers vary

4. **(a)** 07:15   **(c)** 12:50   **(e)** 18:45
   (b) 00:20   **(d)** 16:25   **(f)** 00:45

5. **(a)** 11.15 a.m. **(b)** 1.20 p.m. **(c)** 7.45 a.m. **(d)** 8.20 p.m. **(e)** 12.15 a.m.

6. 7 hours and 30 minutes.

7. 6 hours and 47 minutes.

8. **(a)** 07:25   **(b)** 07:55   **(c)** 08:28

9. **(a)** Fast train 1 h 55 mins / slow train 3 h 35 mins → difference in journey time of 1 hour 40 mins

   (b) 15:58   **(c)** 14:18

Exercise 9.2

1. **(a)** $\frac{1}{30}$ **(b)** $\frac{1}{12}$ **(c)** $\frac{1}{3}$ **(d)** $\frac{11}{12}$

2. **(a)** 10 minutes   **(b)** 24 minutes   **(c)** 35 minutes   **(d)** 9 minutes

3. 120 minutes

4. 4 hours and 9 minutes

5. **(a)** $3\frac{1}{12}$ hours   **(b)** 3 hours and 5 minutes

6. 25 minutes

7. 42 minutes

8. 25 minutes

9. **(a)** $\frac{1}{12}$ **(b)** $\frac{1}{3}$ **(c)** $\frac{1}{6}$ **(d)** $\frac{1}{6}$ (assembly and break)

Exercise 9.3

1.

Name	Finish Time
Louis	10m 5s
Henry	10m 50s
Charles	11m 14s
Oliver	11m 27s

2. Louis

3. Ollie

4. James

5. They both finish together.

6. Nickie, Ollie, Mona

Exercise 9.4

1.	50 km/h	**5.**	3 km/h	**9.**	12 miles/h
2.	5 km/h	**6.**	300 km/h	**10.**	24 km/h
3.	20 miles/h	**7.**	105 miles/h	**11.**	Coach
4.	60 km/h	**8.**	10 km/h	**12.**	The girl
				13.	The train

Exercise 9.5

1.	100 km	**4.**	2 km	**7.**	240 km
2.	50 km	**5.**	75 km	**8.**	30 km
3.	5 miles	**6.**	75 km	**9.**	270 km

Exercise 9.6

1.	2 hours	**6.**	3 hours
2.	30 minutes	**7.**	36 minutes
3.	20 minutes	**8.**	1 hour and 12 minutes
4.	36 minutes	**9.**	40 minutes
5.	40 minutes	**10.**	1 hour and 30 minutes

Exercise 9.7

1. 220 miles/h

2. 5 hours and 40 minutes.

3. Cheetah: $1\frac{2}{3}$ km/min; sprinter: 720 m/min, so cheetah is faster.
To run 10 km: cheetah: 6 minutes; sprinter: 13.9 minutes.

4. Distance 165 km; journey time $3\frac{1}{2}$ h; arrive 1200

5. 44 miles/h

6. About $12\frac{1}{2}$ miles/h

7. The car travelling to London.

Exercise 9.8: Extension question

1. **(a)** 15/03/03

   (b) 12/04/03; 24/04/03

   (c) November and December (12) we have 12 and 03 both factors of 24th (and 12th).

   (d) January and March would have had the most; July, August and October would have had the least.

2. **(a)** This depends on the date!

   Check the answer.
   Assume the century begins 01/01/00
   Year 2000 none
   Year 2001: 10/11/01
   Year 2002: 20/11/02

   (b) Do not be caught out
   by 31/11/13 November
   only has 30 days.
   Then you will have:
   01/11/10, 11/11/11, 21/11/12
   02/11/20, 12/11/21, 22/11/22
   03/11/30, 13/11/31, 23/11/32
   04/11/40, 14/11/41, 24/11/42

3. **(a)** 01/01/03; 03/01/03; 01/03/03; 03/03/03

   (b) 01/01/04; 02/01/04; 04/01/04 also 01/02/04; 02/02/04; 01/04/04; 02/04/04; 04/04/04

   (c) 03/11/99; 09/11/99; 11/11/99

4. **(a)** 19/05/95

   (b) 23/04/92

   (c) 20/03/60; 15/04/60; 12/05/60; 10/06/60; 06/10/60; 05/12/60

   (d) 1924

5. 2 years, 5 months and 9 days

Exercise 9.9: Summary exercise

1. **(a)** 07:25   **(b)** 15:45   **(c)** 00:20   **(d)** 16:15   **(e)** 21:40

2. **(a)** 8.00 p.m.   **(b)** 4.15 a.m.   **(c)** 3.20 p.m.   **(d)** 12.40 a.m.

3. **(a)** 2 hours and 35 minutes.   **(b)** Victoria Embankment to Chelsea Harbour.   **(c)** 13:15

4. 16:08

5. **(a)** 240 miles   **(b)** 80 miles

6. **(a)** $\frac{1}{12}$ **(b)** $\frac{5}{12}$ **(c)** $\frac{3}{5}$

7. **(a)** 75 minutes   **(b)** 204 minutes   **(c)** 140 minutes

8. 93 km/h

9. **(a)** 3 hours and 19 minutes   **(b)** 5 hours and 19 minutes

End of chapter 9 activities: Puzzles

1. **Crossing the lines**

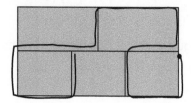

It cannot be done with 3 lines,
you need 4.

2. **The tennis court puzzle**

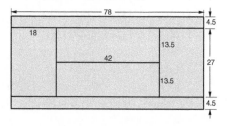 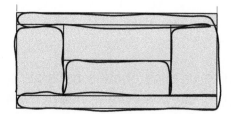

523.5 (unless you can find a shorter distance!)

3. **The fly's tour**

4. **Footprints in the snow**

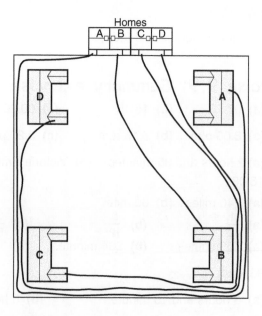

Chapter 10: Charts and tables

Exercise 10.1

1. **(a)**

How many pets do you have?	Tally	Frequency
0	IIII–II	7
1	IIII	4
2	IIII	4
3	III	3
4		0
5	I	I
6		0
7		0
8	I	I
	Total	20

(b)   A bar chart to show how many pets people have.

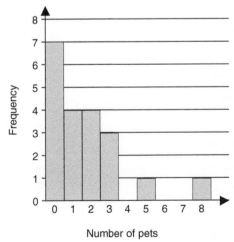

2. Check pupils' answers.

3. (a) Cat

(b) 3

(c) 21

(d) Some children have no pets and some children have more than 1.

4. (a) 92

(b) 180

(c) Staff cars

(d) Open for discussion. Probably get parents to share transport.

5. (a)

Favourite Group	Tally	Frequency
Hotplay	ⵘⵘ ⵘⵘ ⵘⵘ III	18
Dryzone	ⵘⵘ ⵘⵘ ⵘⵘ ⵘⵘ III	23
Club 9	ⵘⵘ II	7
The What	IIII	4
Other	ⵘⵘ III	8
	Total	60

(b)   A bar chart to show favourite pop groups.

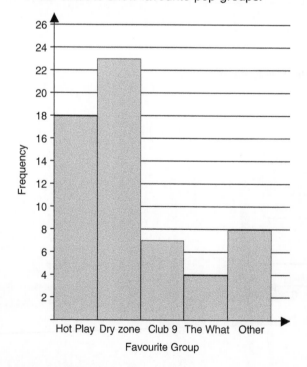

6. Check pupils' answers.

Exercise 10.2

1. **(a)** Ash 25 points; Beech 35 points; Cherry 30 points; Deal 20 points.

(b)

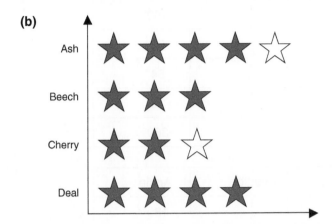

2. **(a)** 9 cheeses

(b) 8 cheeses

(c) 48 cheeses

(d) People are shopping for the weekend

(e) Check pupils' own symbols – probably

Exercise 10.3

1. **(a)** $\frac{2}{3}$

   (b) 40 boys

2. **(a)** $\frac{1}{2}$

   (b) $\frac{1}{4}$

   (c) 60°

   (d) $\frac{1}{12}$

   (e) Car 120; train 20; bus 40; walk 60.

3. **(a)** 40 children

   (b) 30 children

   (c) 35 children

4. **(a)** 40 minibeasts

   (b) 5 woodlice

   (c) $\frac{3}{8}$, 15 centipedes

Exercise 10.4

1.

Favourite lesson	Frequency	Fraction	Angle
Games	10	$\frac{1}{2}$	180°
ICT	5	$\frac{1}{4}$	90°
Art	3	$\frac{3}{20}$	54°
Drama	2	$\frac{1}{10}$	36°
Total	20	1	360°

2.

Favourite colour	Frequency	Fraction	Angle
Blue	18	$\frac{1}{2}$	180°
Red	12	$\frac{1}{3}$	120°
Green	6	$\frac{1}{6}$	60°
Total	36	1	360°

3.

Holiday destination	Frequency	Fraction	Angle
France	8	$\frac{1}{3}$	120°
Britain	6	$\frac{1}{4}$	90°
USA	4	$\frac{1}{6}$	60°
Spain	3	$\frac{1}{8}$	45°
Other	3	$\frac{1}{8}$	45°
Total	24	1	360°

4.

Colour	Frequency	Fraction	Angle
Red	11	$\frac{11}{36}$	110°
Blue	1	$\frac{1}{36}$	10°
White	16	$\frac{4}{9}$	160°
Yellow	4	$\frac{1}{9}$	40°
Silver	4	$\frac{1}{9}$	40°
Total	36	1	360°

5.

Tree	Frequency	Fraction	Angle
Beech	10	$\frac{5}{18}$	100°
Oak	4	$\frac{1}{9}$	40°
Fir	13	$\frac{13}{36}$	130°
Pine	6	$\frac{1}{6}$	60°
Other	3	$\frac{1}{12}$	30°
Total	36	1	360°

6.

Eye colour	Frequency	Fraction	Angle
Blue	8	$\frac{4}{9}$	160°
Brown	6	$\frac{1}{3}$	120°
Grey	3	$\frac{1}{6}$	60°
Green	1	$\frac{1}{18}$	20°
Total	18	1	360°

Exercise 10.5: Extension questions

1.

Hair colour	Frequency
Blonde	6
Red	2
Brown	12
Black	4
Total	24

2.

Colour	Frequency
Red	10
Yellow	6
Silver	12
Blue	3
No bicycle	5
Total	36

3.

No. of people	Tally	Frequency	Fraction	Angle
1	II	2	$\frac{1}{15}$	24°
2	IIII	4	$\frac{1}{15}$	48°
3	HIT	5	$\frac{1}{6}$	60°
4	HIT HIT	10	$\frac{1}{3}$	120°
5	HIT I	6	$\frac{1}{5}$	72°
More than 5	III	3	$\frac{1}{10}$	36°
Total	30	30	1	360°

4.

People in car	Cars	Total no.
1	5	5
2	11	22
3	3	9
4	1	4

Exercise 10.6: Summary exercise

1. **(a)**

No. of brothers and sisters	Tally	Frequency
0	IIII	4
1	HH II	7
2	HH	5
3	III	3
4	I	1
	Total	20

(b) A bar chart to illustrate the number of brothers and sisters

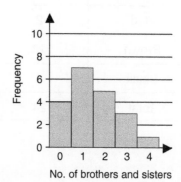

No. of brothers and sisters

2. **(a)**

Garden?	Tally	Frequency	Fraction	Angle
Yes	ⅢⅢ ⅢⅢ I	11	$\frac{11}{20}$	198°
No	ⅢⅢ IIII	9	$\frac{9}{20}$	162°
	Total	20	1	360°

(b) Do you have a garden?

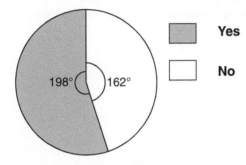

Yes

No

3. **(a)** 20
(b) $\frac{1}{4}$
(c) 8

4. **(a)** 8 hours
(b) $\frac{1}{4}$
(c) 1 hour
(d) 5 hours

End of chapter 10 activity: Statistical surveys

Care should be taken that the questions are phrased to get honest answers. Encourage questions that will not give too many different answers which will be hard to analyse.

Use this opportunity to get some good material for a classroom display.

Chapter 11: Below zero, or negative numbers

Exercise 11.1

1. 240 m
2. −60 m
3. 125 m
4. −25 m
5. The height of the pine tree is about 50 m.
   The top of pine tree is about 140 m above sea level.
6. −40 m

Exercise 11.2

A −20

B −16

C −10

D −4

E 4

F 16

G 25

H 31

Exercise 11.3

1. £4 in credit
2. £5 in credit
3. £15 in debit
4. £5 in debit
5. £12 in credit

Exercise 11.4

Draw a copy of the above number line in your book and mark on it the following numbers:

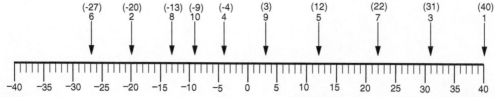

Exercise 11.5

1. 3 + 4 = 7
2. −3 + 4 = 1
3. −5 + 8 = 3
4. −2 + 8 = 6
5. −12 + 5 = −7
6. −3 + 9 = 6
7. −7 + 3 = −4
8. −6 + 9 = 3
9. −2 + 10 = 8
10. −13 + 6 = −7

Exercise 11.6

1.	$7 - 3 = 4$	7.	$6 - 10 = -4$	13.	$2 - 5 = -3$
2.	$7 - 9 = -2$	8.	$4 - 11 = -7$	14.	$-10 - 3 = -13$
3.	$7 - 11 = -4$	9.	$-3 - 5 = -8$	15.	$6 - 8 = -2$
4.	$4 - 3 = 1$	10.	$-6 - 7 = -13$	16.	$-1 - 6 = -7$
5.	$3 - 8 = -5$	11.	$-4 - 8 = -12$	17.	$6 - 7 = -1$
6.	$5 - 9 = -4$	12.	$-3 - 9 = -12$	18.	$8 - 3 = 5$

Exercise 11.7

1.	$5 + (-4) = 1$	7.	$5 + (-9) = -4$	13.	$-1 - (+6) = -7$
2.	$4 + (-2) = 2$	8.	$3 + (-4) = -1$	14.	$-1 + (-9) = -10$
3.	$3 + (-1) = 2$	9.	$7 + (-9) = -2$	15.	$-3 + (-9) = -12$
4.	$-3 + (-4) = -7$	10.	$-6 - (+4) = -10$	16.	$-4 + (-7) = -11$
5.	$-5 + (-6) = -11$	11.	$-1 + (-5) = -6$	17.	$19 + (-3) = 16$
6.	$4 - (+4) = 0$	12.	$-3 + (-7) = -10$	18.	$-15 + (-11) = -26$

Exercise 11.8

1.	$5 - (-1) = 6$	7.	$4 - (-3) = 7$	13.	$-3 - (-6) = 3$
2.	$7 - (-2) = 9$	8.	$-5 - (-2) = -3$	14.	$9 - (+3) = 6$
3.	$-3 - (-3) = 0$	9.	$3 - (-7) = 10$	15.	$12 - (-6) = 18$
4.	$-4 - (-2) = -2$	10.	$5 - (+1) = 4$	16.	$23 - (+15) = 8$
5.	$-6 - (-3) = -3$	11.	$-6 - (-4) = -2$	17.	$-32 - (-26) = -6$
6.	$9 - (-4) = 13$	12.	$1 - (+8) = -7$	18.	$20 - (+16) = 4$

Exercise 11.9

1.	$-4 - 4 = -8$	9.	$-5 - (-3) = -2$	17.	$-7 - (+3) = -10$
2.	$6 - 7 = -1$	10.	$3 + 5 = 8$	18.	$-4 + 9 = 5$
3.	$-4 - (+6) = -10$	11.	$-4 - 6 = -10$	19.	$-7 - 5 = -12$
4.	$-1 + (-3) = -4$	12.	$3 - 12 = -9$	20.	$3 - 12 = -9$
5.	$-5 - (-4) = -1$	13.	$-6 + (-5) = -11$	21.	$-9 + 4 = -5$
6.	$4 + (-2) = 2$	14.	$-5 + (-4) = -9$	22.	$5 - (-5) = 10$
7.	$-3 - (+2) = -5$	15.	$3 - (-9) = 12$	23.	$5 - 5 = 0$
8.	$1 + (-6) = -5$	16.	$-2 + (-4) = -6$	24.	$-5 - 5 = -10$

Exercise 11.10

1. A (2, 9);   E (−7, −6);
    B (−6, 5);   F (−3, 3);
    C (6, −5);   G (6, 6);
    D (−4, 0);   H (10, −8);
                       J (5, 0).

2. **(a)** Rectangle   **(d)** Square
    (b) Rhombus   **(e)** Kite
    (c) Parallelogram   **(f)** Trapezium

3.
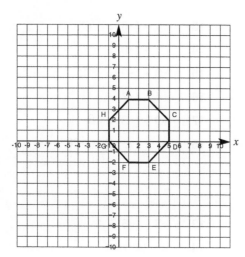

4.
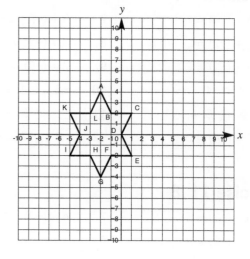

5.
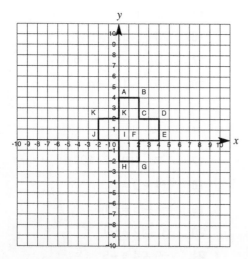

6. **(a)**
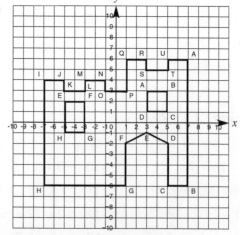

(b) Various answers possible:
Window 1: A (3, 3); B (5, 3); C (5, 1);
D (3, 1).
Window 2: E (−5, 2); F (−3, 2);
G (−3, −1); H (−5, −1).

7.(a)

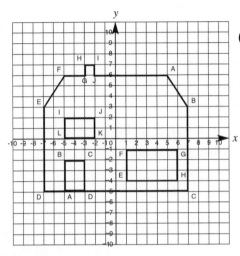

(b) Various answers possible:

Example:

Door:

$A(-5, -5)$, $B(-5, -1)$, $C(-3, -1)$, $D(-3, -5)$

Window 1:

$E(1, -4)$, $F(1, -1)$, $G(6, -1)$, $H(6, -4)$

Window 2:

$I(-5, 2)$, $J(-2, 2)$, $K(-2, 0)$, $L(-5, 0)$

Exercise 11.11

1. **(a)** 6 units right, 1 unit down.
   (b) 5 units right, 5 units up.
   (c) 5 units right, 2 units down.
   (d) 0 units right, 7 units down.
   (e) 6 units left, 8 units up.

2. **(a)** 6 units right, 1 unit down.
   (b) 3 units right, 0 units down.
   (c) 6 units right, 5 units up.
   (d) 0 units right, 6 units down.
   (e) 7 units right, 1 unit down.
   (f) 7 units left, 7 units up.

3.

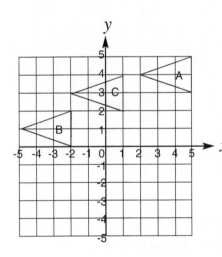

(a) See diagram for B

(b) Triangle B co-ordinates: $(-5, 1)$, $(-2, 2)$, $(-2, 0)$

(c) See diagram for C

(d) Triangle C co-ordinates: $(-2, 3)$, $(1, 4)$, $(1, 2)$

(e) Translation to Map C to A is 4 right and 1 up.

4.

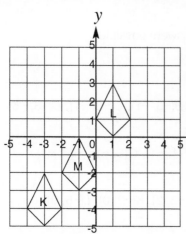

(a) See diagram for kite L.

(b) Kite L vertices: (0, 1), (1, 3), (2, 1), (1, 0).

(c) See diagram for kite M.

(d) Kite M (−1, 0), (−2, −2), (−1, −3), (0, −2).

(e) Translation to Map M to K is 2 left and 2 down.

Exercise 11.12

1. (a) In the *y* axis.

(b) 90°anticockwise about the origin.

(c) 6 units right, 6 units up.

2.

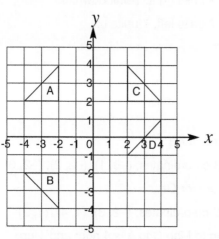

3.

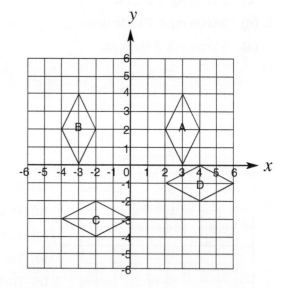

(a) See diagram for B.

(b) See diagram for C.

(c) See diagram for D.

(d) Co-ordinates of D: (4, 1), (4, −1), (2, −1).

(a) Rhombus.

(b) See diagram for B.

(c) See diagram for C.

(d) See diagram for D

(e) Co-ordinates for D:

(2, −1), (4, 0), (6, −1), (4, −2)

Exercise 11.13: Extension questions

1. **(a)** A (−4, 0); B (−2, 1); C (0, 2); D (2, 3); E (4, 4).

   (b) x co-ordinates add on 2, and y co-ordinates add 1 each time.

   (c) (i) (6, 5); (ii) (34, 19)

   (d) (14, 9)

   (e) (i) No   (ii) Yes   (iii) No

   (f) (i) (40, 22)   (ii) (−10, −3)   (iii) (−18, −7)

2. **(a)** (i) Yes   (ii) No   (iii) Yes

   (b) (i) (11, −17)   (ii) (201, −302)   (iii) (13, −20)

3. **(a)** Diamond   **(c)** Spade   **(e)** Club   **(g)** Club

   (b) Spade   **(d)** Spade   **(f)** Club   **(h)** Diamond

4. **(a)** (−4, 0)   **(c)** (0, 7)   **(e)** (−2, −2)   **(g)** (−7, −2)

   (b) (1, 8)   **(d)** (−8, −3)   **(f)** (−2, 9)   **(h)** (−11, 1)

Exercise 11.14: Summary exercise

1. **(a)** 4   **(d)** 2

   (b) 2   **(e)** −2

   (c) 2   **(f)** −2

2. **(a)** −3 − 7 = −10   **(f)** −25 + (−15) = −40

   (b) 5 − (−6) = 11   **(g)** 13 + (−11) = 2

   (c) 9 − 10 = −1   **(h)** −3 + 12 = 9

   (d) −6 − (+7) = −13   **(i)** 10 − 8 = 2

   (e) −6 + (−2) = −8   **(j)** 4 − (−8) = 12

3. 3 − (−2) = 3 + 2 = 5

   2 − (−2) = 2 + 2 = 4

   1 − (−2) = 1 + 2 = 3

   0 − (−2) = 0 + 2 = 2

   −1 − (−2) = −1 + 2 = 1

   −2 − (−2) = −2 + 2 = 0

4. Hexagon

5. Either (6, 3) and (6, –2) or (–4, 3) and (–4, –2)

6. (5, 1) or (–3, 6) or (–3, –4)

7.

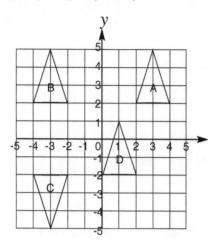

(a) See diagram for triangle A.

(b) See diagram for triangle B.

(c) See diagram for triangle C.

(d) See diagram for triangle D.

Note: make sure pupils have drawn this axes with one centimetre for one unit.

End of Chapter 11 activity: The Balloon Game

Practical. Use the worksheet for the game and cards.

This game has been around for some time in a variety of forms. It is not a game of skill but purely of chance. Some of your pupils may like to analyse the probability of getting across the chasm without disaster.

Chapter 12: Introducing algebra

Exercise 12.1

1. $8 + 3 = 11$
2. $15 - 5 = 10$
3. $7 + 6 = 13$
4. $12 + 8 = 20$
5. $15 - 6 = 9$
6. $12 - 9 = 3$
7. $3 + 1 = 4$
8. $19 + 6 = 25$
9. $20 - 14 = 6$
10. $12 + 6 = 18$

11. $2 \times 7 = 14$
12. $18 \div 6 = 3$
13. $6 \times 5 = 30$
14. $24 \div 4 = 6$
15. $3 \times 7 = 21$
16. $27 \div 3 = 9$
17. $36 \div 6 = 6$
18. $7 \times 8 = 56$
19. $3 \times 10 = 30$
20. $72 \div 8 = 9$

Exercise 12.2

1. $x = 7$
2. $x = 14$
3. $x = 5$
4. $x = 9$
5. $x = 6$
6. $x = 19$
7. $x = 6$
8. $x = 21$
9. $x = 23$
10. $x = 10$
11. $x = 3$
12. $x = 8$
13. $x = 5$
14. $x = 9$
15. $x = 5$
16. $x = 64$
17. $x = 3$
18. $x = 4$
19. $x = 12$
20. $x = 11$
21. $x = 1$
22. $x = 9$
23. $x = 9$
24. $x = 104$
25. $x = 8$
26. $x = 6$

Exercise 12.3

1. $4a$
2. $2b$
3. $6b$
4. $5x$
5. $3y$
6. $3y$
7. $5b$
8. $7a$
9. $2x$
10. $2y$
11. $2x$
12. $6a$
13. $2b$
14. c
15. $3y$
16. x

Exercise 12.4

1. $-2a$
2. $-x$
3. $3a$
4. $3a + 2b$
5. $9a - 3b$
6. $b + 3c$
7. $7a$
8. $6a + 5b$
9. 0
10. $-x + y$; $y - x$
11. $3a - 3b$
12. $3x + y$
13. $5x - y$
14. $3x + 2y$
15. $2b - a$
16. $7x - 9y$
17. $7a + 2c$
18. $-x$
19. $6b$
20. $7a - 3b$

Exercise 12.5

1. $3a + 4$
2. $3x - 2$
3. $2x + 3$
4. $2b - 3$
5. $2c + 7$
6. $6a + 2$
7. $4b - 1$
8. -1
9. 0
10. 0

Exercise 12.6

1. $8a$
2. x
3. $\dfrac{c}{3}$
4. $\dfrac{3x}{2}$
5. 0
6. 0
7. $5x$
8. $4a$
9. $\dfrac{4b}{5}$
10. $3b - c$
11. 2
12. $\dfrac{3b}{2}$
13. $2c$
14. $6x$
15. $6a$

Exercise 12.7

1. $a = 5$
2. $b = 3$
3. $c = 6$
4. $d = 4$
5. $a = \dfrac{1}{3}$
6. $b = \dfrac{2}{5}$
7. $a = 10$
8. $c = 12$
9. $b = 7\dfrac{1}{2}$
10. $x = 2\dfrac{2}{3}$
11. $a = 1\dfrac{2}{3}$
12. $c = -6$
13. $b = 1\dfrac{3}{4}$
14. $x = -4$
15. $y = \dfrac{-2}{3}$

Exercise 12.8

1. $x = 2$
2. $a = 2$
3. $b = 2$
4. $c = 2$
5. $x = 2$
6. $x = 6$
7. $a = 1\dfrac{4}{5}$
8. $b = 3$
9. $c = 4$
10. $x = 1\dfrac{3}{4}$
11. $y = 3$
12. $a = -2$
13. $b = 3$
14. $c = \dfrac{1}{2}$
15. $x = 3$
16. $y = 3$
17. $a = \dfrac{4}{5}$
18. $b = -1$
19. $c = \dfrac{1}{2}$
20. $x = -2$

Exercise 12.9

1. 3
2. 3 games
3. 54%
4. 17 bloomed overnight
5. 27 chocolates

6. 11 eggs
7. 7 conkers
8. 88 kg
9. 36 sweets
10. 11 years old

Exercise 12.10

1. 18
2. 6 m
3. 26 lengths
4. 6 circuits

5. £2.50
6. 52 years old
7. 14 years old
8. 42 years old

Exercise 12.11: Extension questions

1. **(a)** $260 - x + x + 150 - x = 410 - x$

   (b) $410 - x = 350, x = 60$

   (c) There are 60 pupils in Year 5.

2. **(a)** 7 kg

   (b) 65 kg

3. 40p

4. **(a)**

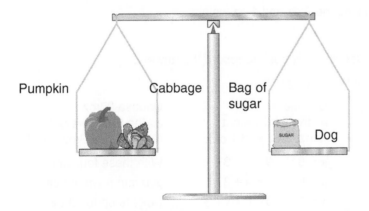

   (b) The dog weighs 9 kg.

Exercise 12.12: Summary exercise

1. **(a)** $a = 2$ **(b)** $b = 9$ **(c)** $c = 5$ **(d)** $d = 10$

2.   **(a)** $3x$ **(b)** $5a$ **(c)** $3b$

3.   **(a)** $5x + 8y$ **(c)** $5a + b$ **(e)** $6c - 7x$
       (b) $5x + 2$ **(d)** a **(f)** $4b - 4$

4.   **(a)** $x = 4$ **(b)** $a = 2\frac{1}{3}$ **(c)** $b = 14$ **(d)** $c = -15$

5.   **(a)** $x = 1$ **(c)** $a = 4$ **(e)** $b = -1\frac{1}{2}$ **(g)** $y = 1$
       (b) $a = -4$ **(d)** $b = 6$ **(f)** $x = \frac{1}{2}$ **(h)** $a = -8$

6.   7 pencils

7.   13 years old

8.   11

9.   42 years old

10.   11 children do both

End of chapter 12 activity: The shopkeeper's dilemma

He should choose the 3 oz and the 1 oz weights.

1 oz could be measured by using the 1 oz weight.

2 oz could be measured by using the 3 oz and by putting the 1 oz weight on the side of the 2 oz being weighed.

3 oz could be measured by using the 3 oz weight.

4 oz could be measured by using the 3 oz and 1 oz weights.

You may wish to introduce algebra at this point to record the anwers:

For example (where x = object being weighed)

Using two weights only (3 oz and 1oz).	Choose 9 oz as the third weight (9 oz, 3 oz and 1 oz).	Choose 27 oz as the fourth weight (27 oz, 9 oz, 3 oz and 1 oz).
$x = 1$ $1 = x$	$x = 5$ $9 = x + 3 + 1$	With these four weights
$x = 2$ $3 = x + 1$	$x = 6$ $9 = x + 3$	you can measure all
$x = 3$ $3 = x$	$x = 7$ $9 + 1 = x + 3$	weights up to 40 oz.
$x = 4$ $3 + 1 = x$	$x = 8$ $9 = x + 1$	$x = 40$ $27 + 9 + 3 + 1 = x$
	$x = 9$ $9 = x$	
	$x = 10$ $9 + 1 = x$	
	$x = 11$ $9 + 3 = x + 1$	
	$x = 12$ $9 + 3 = x$	
	$x = 13$ $9 + 3 + 1 = x$	

Chapter 13: Calculating with and without a calculator

Exercise 13.1

1. $3 \times 2 + 7 = 13$
2. $3 + 2 \times 7 = 17$
3. $6 + 5 \times 3 = 21$
4. $6 \times 5 + 3 = 33$
5. $10 - 2 \times 3 = 4$
6. $2 + 5 \times 6 = 32$
7. $(2 + 5) \times 6 = 42$
8. $2 + (5 \times 6) = 32$
9. $\frac{1}{5}$ of $25 = 5$
10. $\frac{1}{4}$ of $12 = 3$
11. $3 \times (2 + 7) = 27$
12. $(3 \times 2) + 7 = 13$
13. $(8 \div 4) - 2 = 0$
14. $8 \div (4 - 2) = 4$
15. $8 \div 4 - 2 = 0$
16. $8 + 4 \times 2 - 5 = 11$

Exercise 13.2

1. $4^2 + 3 \times 5 = 31$
2. $3^3 \div (5 - 2) = 9$
3. $2^3 \div 4 - 2 = 0$
4. $(4 - 2)^2 = 4$
5. $2^3 \div (4 - 2) = 4$
6. $(3^2 - 2^3)^2 = 1$

Exercise 13.3

1. 18 legs
2. 37
3. 19 games
4. 2 toffees each
5. £4
6. £27
7. 55 years old

Exercise 13.4

1. 364 apples
2. £174.42
3. (a) 481
   (b) 961, so (b) is greater by 480
4. £12.48
5. 141
6. 18 000
7. 46
8. 2124 m
9. 365
10. 42 143 (Note the answer does not say pairs of trainers; 4958 scarves, 9437 shirts and 29748 trainers.)

Exercise 13.5: Mark my work!

1. $(13 - 2) \times 5 = 55$

2. $13 \times 161 = 2093$

3.   Should be either $200\ 000 = 2 \times 10^5$ or $20\ 000 = 2 \times 10^4$

4. $50 \times 20 = 1000$

5.   MCMXCV is 1995

6.   Same time if in same pot.

7. $52 \times 48 \approx 2500$

8. $(3 + 5) \times (2 + 3) \quad = 8 \times 5$

$= 40$

9.   If one bus takes 46 passengers, it will take 2 buses to take 92 passengers.

10.   In ten years there are 3650 days: not necessarily because of leap years.

11.   It takes 5 men 20 days to build a house and so it takes one man 100 days.

12. $10^3 \times 10^3 = 10^6$

13. $2 + (5 \times 6) - (4 \div 2) = 30$

14. $30\ 000 \div 60 = 500$

15. $122 \div 28 \approx 120 \div 30 = 40$

Exercise 13.6: Extension questions

1.   240 pints

2.   4950 m

3.   2500

4.   480 bricks

5.   290

6.   **(a)** The first deal

      (b) The first deal

      (c) The second deal

7.   **(a)** 3990 shillings

      (b) 2821 shillings

Exercise 13.7: Summary exercise

1.   **(a)** $(3 + 5) \times 4 = 32$ **(c)** $12 \div (4 + 2) = 2$ **(e)** $24 \div (8 - 2) = 4$

      (b) $3 + 5 \times 4 = 23$ **(d)** $12 \div 4 + 2 = 5$ **(f)** $24 \div 8 - 2 = 1$

2.   27 days

3.   604 800

4.   129 600 miles

5.   £30.72

6.   £89.50

7.   £48.70

End of chapter activities: Think of a number

1. **Puzzle 1: An amazing puzzle**

   Whatever number is chosen in (a) when multiplied by 9 in (b), will give you a two digit number. The sum of the two digits number created in (b) will be 9. Subtracting 5 from the number created in (c) will always be 4 (d). The fourth letter of the alphabet in (e) is D, and the only country in Europe starting with D is Denmark. In (g) you choose an animal that starts with the letter K and in (h) you choose a colour that starts with the last letter of your animal. Some people end up with Amber Koala from Denmark, but most pick Orange Kangaroos!

2. **Puzzle 2: A Number Trick**

   Try letting the number be x

   Then you have

   (a) x

   (b) $2x$

   (c) $40 + 2x$

   (d) $2000 + 100x$

   Now suppose your birthday is 30th October 1993.

   On 1st February you have not had your birthday so:

   (e) $2004 + 100x$

   (f) $11 + 100x$

   Written as a 3 digit number this will look:

   $x11$

   x is the number they chose and 11 is their age.

Chapter 14: More decimals

Exercise 14.1

1. $0.4 \times 4 = 1.6$
2. $1.4 \times 3 = 4.2$
3. $3.2 \times 7 = 22.4$
4. $0.16 \times 5 = 0.8$
5. $3.5 \times 2 = 7$
6. $0.4 \times 70 = 28$
7. $2.6 \times 50 = 130$
8. $4.2 \times 30 = 126$
9. $1.6 \times 20 = 32$

10. $1.5 \times 6 = 9$
11. $4.8 \times 7 = 33.6$
12. $0.35 \times 8 = 2.8$
13. $10.3 \times 6 = 61.8$
14. $8.12 \times 9 = 73.08$
15. $0.15 \times 800 = 120$
16. $20.1 \times 40 = 804$
17. $0.07 \times 900 = 63$
18. $4.5 \times 20 = 90$

19. $10.4 \times 5 = 52$
20. $6.03 \times 8 = 48.24$
21. $4.15 \times 2 = 8.3$
22. $3.5 \times 9 = 31.5$
23. $1.7 \times 4 = 6.8$
24. $6.2 \times 30 = 186$
25. $1.7 \times 700 = 1190$
26. $3.09 \times 40 = 123.6$
27. $7.9 \times 800 = 6320$

Exercise 14.2

1. $0.3 \times 0.6 = 0.18$
2. $0.3 \times 0.06 = 0.018$
3. $0.03 \times 0.006 = 0.00018$
4. $0.06 \times 3 = 0.18$
5. $0.7 \times 0.2 = 0.14$
6. $6.3 \times 5 = 31.5$
7. $8.1 \times 0.12 = 0.972$
8. $1.02 \times 0.07 = 0.0714$
9. $0.002 \times 0.4 = 0.0008$

10. $0.12 \times 0.4 = 0.048$
11. $0.42 \times 0.3 = 0.126$
12. $0.24 \times 3 = 0.72$
13. $0.11 \times 5 = 0.55$
14. $1.2 \times 0.4 = 0.48$
15. $4.2 \times 0.7 = 2.94$
16. $10.2 \times 0.5 = 5.1$
17. $12.2 \times 3.4 = 41.48$
18. $45.2 \times 4.2 = 189.84$

19. $1.3 \times 1.2 = 1.56$
20. $3.2 \times 0.4 = 1.28$
21. $4.5 \times 2 = 9$
22. $0.5 \times 0.4 = 0.2$
23. $1.5 \times 6 = 9$
24. $24 \times 0.33 = 7.92$
25. $12.5 \times 0.08 = 1$
26. $4.5 \times 1.2 = 5.4$
27. $0.36 \times 0.025 = 0.009$

Exercise 14.3

1. $1.5 \div 3 = 0.5$
2. $0.27 \div 9 = 0.03$
3. $0.35 \div 5 = 0.07$
4. $1.2 \div 4 = 0.3$
5. $1.44 \div 12 = 0.12$

6. $0.036 \div 6 = 0.006$
7. $6.4 \div 8 = 0.8$
8. $4.5 \div 9 = 0.5$
9. $0.72 \div 12 = 0.06$
10. $0.066 \div 11 = 0.006$

11. $2.8 \div 7 = 0.4$
12. $4.2 \div 7 = 0.6$
13. $0.018 \div 2 = 0.009$
14. $1.32 \div 11 = 0.12$
15. $0.108 \div 12 = 0.009$

Exercise 14.4

1. $1.071 \div 17 = 0.063$

2. $103.5 \div 23 = 4.5$

3. $20.40 \div 24 = 0.85$

4. $2.257 \div 37 = 0.061$

5. $0.2624 \div 41 = 0.0064$

6. $285.6 \div 51 = 5.6$

7. $15.04 \div 16 = 0.94$

8. $1.566 \div 27 = 0.058$

9. $0.3888 \div 72 = 0.0054$

10. $13.44 \div 21 = 0.64$

11. $0.770 \div 22 = 0.035$

12. $1.968 \div 16 = 0.123$

13. $42.12 \div 13 = 3.24$

14. $13.416 \div 24 = 0.559$

15. $1.3014 \div 18 = 0.0723$

16. $1.5 \div 2 = 0.75$

17. $0.7 \div 4 = 0.175$

18. $0.03 \div 6 = 0.005$

19. $0.6 \div 12 = 0.05$

20. $1.05 \div 4 = 0.2625$

21. $2.01 \div 12 = 0.1675$

22. $0.21 \div 6 = 0.035$

23. $1.08 \div 12 = 0.09$

24. $0.72 \div 5 = 0.144$

25. $0.0027 \div 18 = 0.00015$

26. $1.03 \div 8 = 0.12875$

27. $12.1 \div 16 = 0.75625$

28. $4.5 \div 8 = 0.5625$

29. $0.405 \div 182 = 0.002225$

30. $0.31 \div 4 = 0.0775$

Exercise 14.5

1. £12.85

2. £1.28

3. £9.89

4. A bag of half a dozen.

5.

4 kg of flour at 63p a kilo	=	£ 2.52
2 kg of sugar at £1.35 a kilo	=	£ 2.70
2 dozen eggs at £1.56 a dozen	=	£ 3.12
Total	=	£ 8.34

6.

6 pencils at 20p each	=	£ 1.20
5 erasers at 35p each	=	£ 1.75
3 sharpeners at 65p each	=	£ 1.95
2 Geometry sets at £1.99 each	=	£ 3.98
Total	=	£ 8.88

7.

2.5 kg of flour at £0.84 a kilo	=	£ 2.10
1.5 kilo of sugar at £ 0.96 a kilo	=	£ 1.44
18 eggs at £1.02 per half dozen	=	£ 3.06
800g of raisins at 42p per 100g	=	£ 3.36
Total	=	£ 9.96

8. **(a)** (i) £4.48   (ii) £3.20   (iii) £9.38

    (b) £15.40

9. 86p

10. Box B

11. The dozen value eggs at £1.80.

12. £340.88

Exercise 14.6

1. **(a)** 156 US$ **(d)** 8500 J$

    (b) 140 Euros   **(e)** 220 SF

    (c) 184 Yen   **(f)** 6200 TB

2. **(a)** £64.10   **(d)** £1.18

    (b) £71.43   **(e)** £45.45

    (c) £54.35   **(f)** £1.61

3. **(a)** 31.20 US$ **(d)** 1700 J$

    (b) 28 Euros   **(e)** 44 SF

    (c) 36.8 Yen   **(f)** 1240 TB

4. **(a)** £32.05   **(d)** £0.35

    (b) £10.71   **(e)** £18.18

    (c) £326.09   **(f)** £10.48

5. **(a)** 28€   **(b)** 11€   **(c)** £7.86

6. **(a)** £64.10   **(b)** £0.10   **(c)** $0.16

7. 2604 TB

Exercise 14.7

1. Teachers may want pupils to use proper graph paper for this exercise.

   (a) (i) 0 lb   (ii) 2.2 lb   (iii) 11 lb

   (b), (c) and **(d)** see graph below.

   (e) (i) 1.4 kg = 3.11 lb

        (ii) 3.0 lb = 1.4 kg

        (iii) 4.5 kg = 9.9 lb

        (iv) 10.5 lb = 4.8 kg

   Note to teachers:
   when checking the graph
   ensure that the line goes
   through the following points

   1 kg = 2.2 lb

   2 kg = 4.4 lb

   3 kg = 6.6 lb

   4 kg = 8.8 lb

   5 kg = 11 lb

Graph to show the conversion of kilogrammes to pounds.

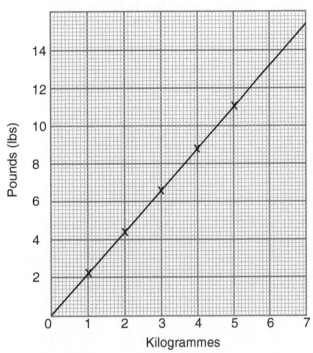

2. **(a)** (i) 0 litre = 0 gallon

        (ii) 5 litres = 1.1 gallons

        (iii) 20 litres = 4.4 gallons

   Note to teachers:
   when checking the graph
   ensure that the line goes
   through the following points

   5 litres = 1.10 gallons

   10 litres = 2.2 gallons

   15 litres = 3.3 gallons

   20 litres = 4.4 gallons

   30 litres = 6.6 gallons

   (b) Graph to show the conversion of litres to gallons.

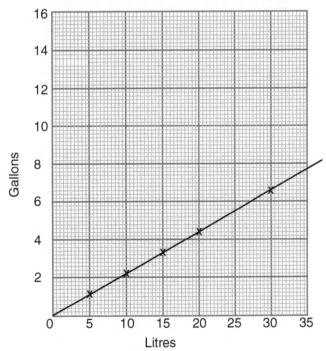

(c) (i) 2.6 gallons   (ii) 13.6 litres   (iii) 5.5 gallons   (iv) 37.3 litres

3. **(a)** (i) J$ 4250   (ii) J$ 8500

(b) See graph below.

(c) (i) £6   (ii) J$ 11 000   (iii) £21   (iv) J$ 7500

Please note that any greater degree of accuracy is difficult to get from a graph such as the one below. The pupils could use twice the scale on the J$ axis. It is not reasonable to expect them to accuracy position 4250 J$. 8500 is just possible.

A graph to show the conversion of pounds to Jamaican dollars.

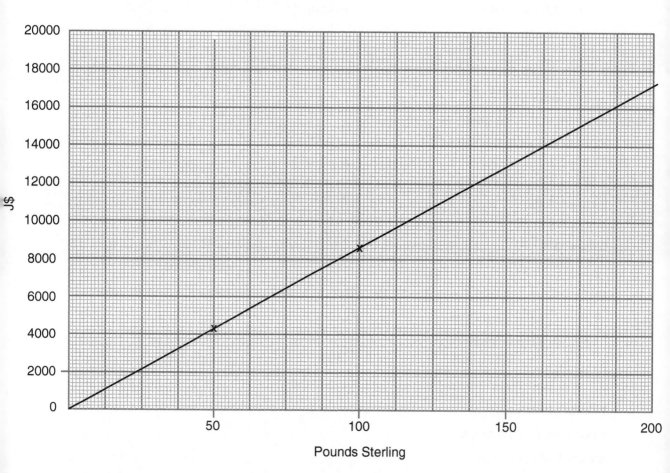

4. A chart to show the conversion from pounds Sterling to United States Dollars.

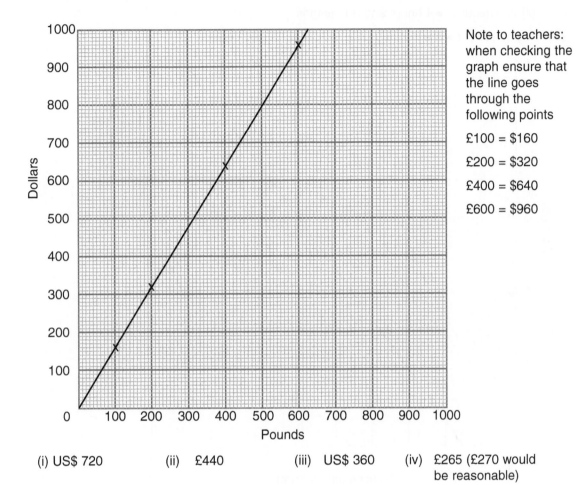

Note to teachers: when checking the graph ensure that the line goes through the following points

£100 = $160

£200 = $320

£400 = $640

£600 = $960

(i) US$ 720   (ii) £440   (iii) US$ 360   (iv) £265 (£270 would be reasonable)

5. **(a)** (i) 135 minutes = 2 hours and 15 minutes

(ii) 270 minutes = 4 hours and 30 minutes

(b) A graph to show the cooking time needed for a joint of lamb

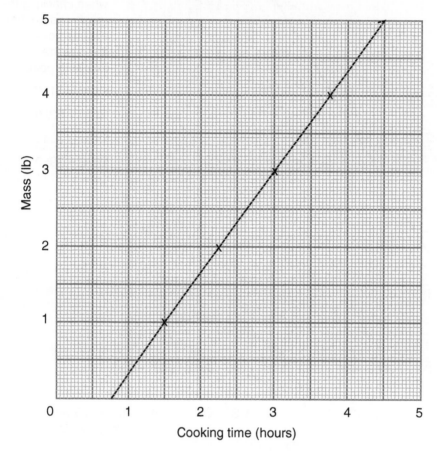

Note to teachers: when checking the graph ensure that the line goes through the following points:

$(1\frac{1}{2}, 1)$; $((2\frac{1}{4}, 2)$; $(3, 3)$; $(3\frac{3}{4}, 4)$

Please note that since it is unrealistic to cook very small masses of meat, it might be appropriate to dot the line below $\frac{1}{2}$ lb.

(c) (i) 3 hours   (ii) 3 hours and 45 minutes

(d) $1\frac{2}{3}$ lb

6. A graph to show the conversion of kilometres into miles.

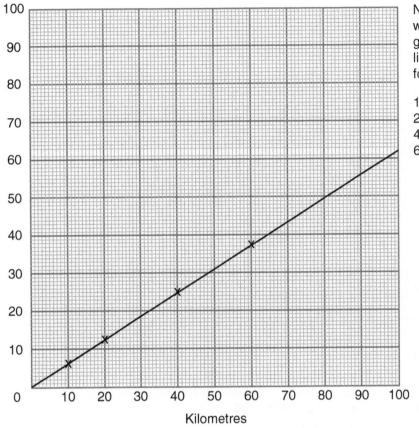

Kilometres

Note to teachers:
when checking the
graph ensure that the
line goes through the
following points

10 km = 6 miles
20 km = 12 miles
40 km = 25 miles
60 km = 37 miles

(a) 40 kilometres

(b) 43.5 miles

(c) 97 kilometres per hour ≈ 100 kilometres per hour

(d) 37 miles per hour ≈ 40 miles per hour

7. **(a)** (i) 0   (ii) 90

(b) A graph to show the conversion from the original mark to the new mark.

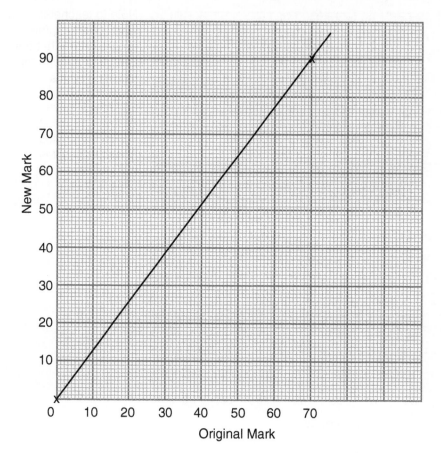

Original Mark

Exercise 14.8: Extension questions - Travel graphs

1. **(a)** 50 km/h: car

(b) $12\frac{1}{2}$ km/h: motorised scooter (or cycle)

(c) $8\frac{1}{3}$ km/h: bicycle (or jogging)

2. **(a)** 60 kilometres per hour **(b)** $7\frac{1}{2}$ kilometres per hour **(c)** $3\frac{1}{3}$ km/h

3. **(a)** 80 kilometres per hour   **(d)** Approx 52 kilometres per hour

(b) It stopped for half an hour.   **(e)** Any reasonable answer is acceptable.

(c) 80 kilometres per hour

4. **(a)** He travelled for 1 hour at 24 kilometres per hour, then accelerated and travelled at 64 kilometres per hour for the next hour. He then rested for half an hour before continuing his journey at 64 kilometres per hour for 42 minutes.

(b) Any reasonable answer is acceptable.

5. See graph below. The journey was 180 miles.

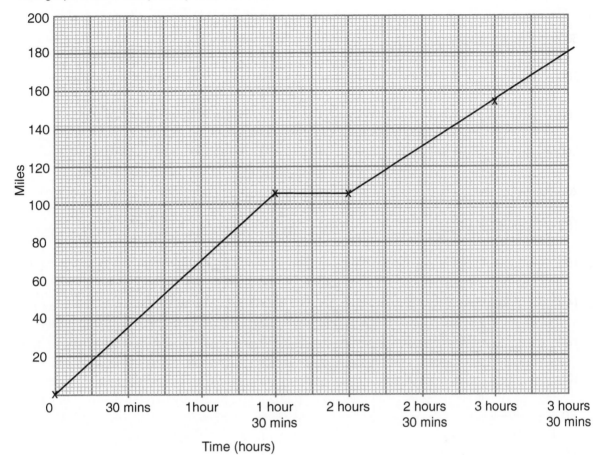

Time (hours)

6. See graph below. The journey was 250 miles.

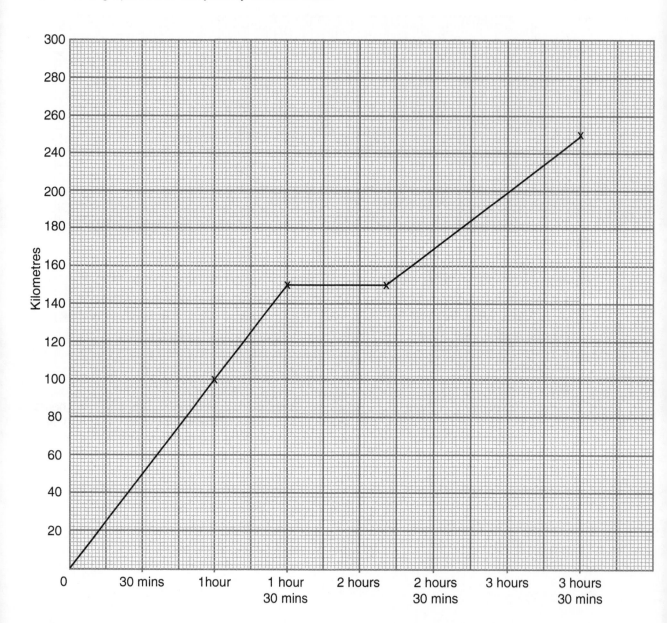

Exercise 14.9: Summary exercise

1. **(a)** 0.8   **(b)** 1.5   **(c)** 3.6   **(d)** 4.9

2. **(a)** 9   **(b)** 200   **(c)** 546   **(d)** 5640

3. **(a)** 0.08   **(b)** 0.18   **(c)** 0.4   **(d)** 0.02

4. **(a)** 0.8   **(b)** 0.2   **(c)** 0.04   **(d)** 0.075

5. **(a)** 0.21   **(b)** 0.124

6. £7.44   **7.** 69p   **8.** 17p

9. Copy and complete this shopping list:

4 kg of carrots at 45p a kilo	=	£ 1.80
2.5 kg of potatoes at 60p a kilo	=	£ 1.50
5 kg of onions at 37 p a kilo	=	£ 1.85
9 avocadoes at £1.35 for 3	=	£ 4.05
Total	=	£ 9.20

10. £250

End of chapter 14 activity: How many nets?

Possible nets of cubes:

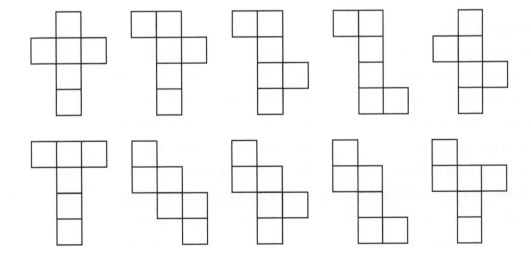

Chapter 15: Area

Exercise 15.1

1. 6 cm by 2 cm = 12 cm²
2. 4 cm by 5 cm = 20 cm²
3. 4 cm by 4 cm = 16 cm²
4. 10 cm by 5 cm = 50 cm²
5. 3 cm by 8 cm = 24 cm²
6. 12 cm by 4 cm = 48 cm²
7. 10 mm by 70 mm = 7 cm²
8. 3 cm by 6 cm = 18 cm²
9. 90 mm by 40 mm = 36 cm²
10. 60 mm by 50 mm = 30 cm²
11. 5 cm by 5 cm = 25 cm²
12. With sides of 10 cm = 100 cm²
13. All sides 7 cm = 49 cm²
14. With sides of 0.5 m = 2500 cm²
15. 0.3 m by 5 m = 1.5 m²
16. 2.5 cm by 6 cm = 15 cm²
17. 0.2 km by 0.2 km = 0.04 km²
18. 3.5 cm by 6 cm = 21 cm²
19. 1.2 km by 0.5 km = 0.6 km²
20. 3.4 cm by 0.9 cm = 3.06 cm²

Exercise 15.2

1. 6 m by 20 cm = 12 000 cm²
2. 4 cm by 50 mm = 20 cm²
3. 400 cm by 4 m = 160 000 cm²
4. 10 cm by 0.5 m = 500 cm²
5. 0.4 m by 80 cm = 3 200 cm²
6. 1.2 m by 400 cm = 48 000 cm²
7. 10 mm by 7 cm = 7 cm²
8. 30 cm by 6 m = 18 000 cm²
9. 50 mm by 0.4 m = 200 cm²
10. 0.4 m by 400 cm = 16 000 cm²

Exercise 15.3

1. 6 cm by 4 cm = 20 cm
2. 3 cm by 5 cm = 16 cm
3. 6 cm by 6 cm = 24 cm
4. 8 cm by 4 cm = 24 cm
5. 5 cm by 7 cm = 24 cm
6. 10 cm by 5 cm = 30 cm
7. 10 mm by 40 mm = 100 mm
8. 2 cm by 7 cm = 18 cm
9. 90 mm by 30 mm = 24 cm
10. 60 mm by 70 mm = 26 cm
11. 7 cm by 7 cm = 28 cm
12. With sides of 10 cm = 40 cm
13. All sides 4 cm = 16 cm
14. With sides of 0.4 m = 1.6 m
15. 0.4 m by 6 m = 12.8 m
16. 3.5 cm by 4 cm = 15 cm
17. 0.3 km by 0.3 km = 1.2 km
18. 3.5 cm by 8 cm = 23 cm
19. 1.2 km by 0.6 km = 3.6 km
20. 2.2 cm by 0.8 cm = 6 cm

Exercise 15.4

1. 5 m by 30 cm = 1 060 cm
2. 6 cm by 50 mm = 22 cm
3. 20 cm by 2 m = 440 cm
4. 20 cm by 0.5 m = 140 cm
5. 0.5 m by 250 cm = 600 cm
6. 1.2 m by 80 cm = 400 cm (4 m)
7. 12 mm by 6 cm = 14.4 cm
8. 300 cm by 4 m = 1 400 cm
9. 50 mm by 0.6 m = 130 cm
10. 0.3 m by 300 cm = 660 cm (6.6 m)

Exercise 15.5: Practice at calculating areas and perimeters

1. **(a)** Area = 28 cm², Perimeter = 22 cm

    (b) Area = 25 cm², Perimeter = 20 cm

    (c) Area = 18 cm², Perimeter = 22 cm

2. **(a)** A = Area = 24 cm², Perimeter = 28 cm

    B = Area = 12 cm², Perimeter = 26 cm

    C = Area = 12 cm², Perimeter = 14 cm

    (b) A

    (c) A

    (d) C

3. Drawings of possible rectangles should have the following dimensions:

    1 × 24, 2 × 12, 3 × 8, 4 × 6

    1 × 24 has largest perimeter, 4 × 6 has shortest perimeter.

4. Drawings of possible rectangles should have the following dimensions:

    1 × 36, 2 × 18, 3 × 12, 4 × 9, 6 × 6.

    1 × 36 has the largest perimeter, 6 × 6 has the shortest perimeter.

5. 10 m × 10 m

6. Square

7. 30 cm × 35 cm (6 photos in each of 7 rows or 7 photos in each of 6 rows in a frame 30 cm × 35 cm)

8. **(a)** A: Area = 9 cm², Perimeter = 20 cm

    B: Area = 16 cm², Perimeter = 20 cm

    C: Area = 21 cm², Perimeter = 20 cm

    D: Area = 24 cm², Perimeter = 20 cm

    E: Area = 25 cm², Perimeter = 20 cm

    (b) None, they are all the same.

    (c) E

    (d) A

9. Drawings of possible rectangles should have the following dimensions:
    $1 \times 8, 2 \times 7, 3 \times 6, 4 \times 5$
    1×8 has the smallest area, 4×5 the largest area.

10. Drawings of possible rectangles should have the following dimensions:
    $1 \times 7, 2 \times 6, 3 \times 5, 4 \times 4$
    4×4 has the largest area, 1×7 the smallest area.

11. The farmer should form a square with 25 fencing units, i.e. 50 m on each side.

12. A square 0.5 m $\times$ 0.5 m

13. A square 180 cm $\times$ 180 cm

Exercise 15.6

1. A: 12 m, B: 9 m, C: 6 m, D: 18 m

2. A: 36 m, B: 48 m, C: 18 m, D: 24 m

3. 2.5 m

4. 30 cm

Exercise 15.7

1. Length = 120 cm, width = 60 cm

2. Length = 25 cm, width = 20 cm

Exercise 15.8

1. 30 m²

2. 147 m²

3. 162 m²

4. 64 m²

5. 650 m²

6. 9600 cm² (0.96 m²)

7. 38.2 m²

8. (a) 176 m²
    (b) 4 400 tiles
    (c) £6 600

Exercise 15.9

1. 12 cm²

2. 20 m²

3. 24 cm²

4. 40 km²

5. 1.12 m²

6. 1400 m²

7. 24 cm²

8. 31 cm²

9. 24 cm²

10. 57 cm²

11. 162 cm²

Exercise 15.10: Extension questions

1. **(a) (b)** and **(c)** see table below:

Rectangle	Total no. of horizontal lines	Total no. of vertical lines	Total no. of rectangles
A	0	0	1
B	1	0	3
C	1	1	9
D	2	1	18
E	2	2	36
F	3	2	60

(d) The patterns use triangle numbers: 1, 3, 6, 10, 15, 21, 28, 36, 45, ...

For x horizontal lines and y vertical lines the number of rectangles is:

$(x+1)^{th}$ triangle number × $(y+1)^{th}$ triangle number

(e) 6th triangle number × 5th triangle number = 21 × 15 = 315

2. **(a)**

Line	Triangle Number
0	1
1	3
2	6
3	10
4	15

(b) 55 Triangle numbers again.

3. 7 horizontal × 7 vertical lines.
So: 8th triangle number × 8th triangle number
So: 36 × 36
Is 1296 squares

4. **(a)** and **(b)**

Lines	Regions
0	1
1	2
2	4
3	7
4	10
5	14

Lines	Regions
6	18
7	
8	
9	
10	

R = 3L-2 for the first 4 lines, then the system breaks down. It then depends on how the lines are drawn.

Exercise 15.11: Summary exercise

1. 60 cm²
2. 25 m²
3. 38 cm
4. 280 cm
5. Area = 240 cm², Perimeter = 64 cm
6. Area = 8000 cm² (0.8 m²), Perimeter = 480 cm (4.8 m)
7. Height = 12 cm
8. Area of wood = 12 900 cm²
9. Area = 4 200 cm² (0.42 m²)

End of chapter 15 activity

Do people with big feet have big hands?

Practical

Another good opportunity for classroom displays. When the data sheet is complete the pupils should draw a chart or graph to display the results. This could also provide an opportunity to use a spreadsheet program on a computer. The pupils should write down their conclusions.

Chapter 16: Triangles, angles and bearings

Exercise 16.1

Check pupils have drawn the triangles accurately, using the method described in the book.

1. $\angle A = 51°$
   $\angle B = 95°$
   $\angle C = 34°$

2. $\angle P = 71°$
   $\angle Q = 38°$
   $\angle R = 71°$

3. $\angle X = 30°$
   $\angle Y = 89°$
   $\angle Z = 61°$

4. 5. and 6. Check side lengths, neatness and accuracy.

Exercise 16.2

1. $\angle B = 70°$ $\angle C = 70°$ BC = 4.8 cm
2. $\angle R = 100°$ RQ = 5.5 cm   PR = 6.8 cm
3. $\angle X = 76°$ $\angle Z = 44°$ XZ = 6.2 cm

4. 5. 6. and 7. Check pupils' triangle drawings for accuracy and neatness.

Exercise 16.3

1. $a = 55°$ (angles on a straight line add up to 180°).
   $b = 55°$ (angles in a triangle add up to 180°).
2. $a = 85°$ (angles in a triangle add up to 180°).
   $b = 23°$ (vertically opposite angles are equal).
   $c = 85°$ (angles in a triangle add up to 180°).
3. $a = 80°$ (vertically opposite angles are equal).
   $b = 100°$ (angles on a straight line add up to 180°).
   $c = 50°$ (angles at a point add up to 360°).
4. $a = 85°$ (angles on a straight line add up to 180°).
   $b = 63°$ (angles in a triangle add up to 180°).
   $c = 85°$ (vertically opposite angles are equal).
   $d = 70°$ (angles in a triangle add up to 180°).

5. $a = 65°$ (angles on a straight line add up to 180°).

$b = 60°$ (angles in a triangle add up to 180°).

$c = 51°$ (angles on a straight line add up to 180°).

$a = 57°$ (angles in a triangle add up to 180°).

6. $w = 65°$ (angles on a straight line add up to 180°).

$x = 51°$ (angles in a triangle add up to 180°).

$y = 224°$ (angles at a point add up to 360°).

Exercise 16.4

1. $x = 75°$ **2.** $x = 101°$

3. $x = 105°$ **5.** $x = 63°$

4. $x = 30°$ **6.** $x = 75°$

Exercise 16.5

1. $x = 144°$ **4.** $x = 74°$

2. $x = 140°$ **5.** $x = 134°$

3. $x = 88°$ **6.** $x = 48°$

Exercise 16.6

1.

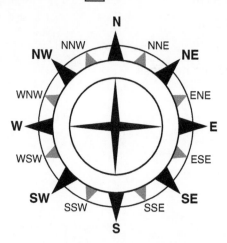

2.

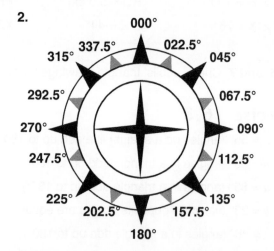

3.

Object	Bearing	Distance	
		Measured	Actual
cow	060°	3.25 cm	32.5 m
sheep	105°	3.1 cm	31 m
farmer	226°	3.2 cm	32 m
tree	310°	3.55 cm	35.5 m

Exercise 16.7

1.   Bearing of B from A is 065°.
     Distance 20 m.

2.   Bearing of B from A is 250°.
     Distance 10 m.

3.   Bearing of B from A is 100°.
     Distance 150 m.

4.   Bearing of B from A is 300°
     Distance 10 m.

5.   Bearing of B from A is 115°.
     Distance 30 m.

6.   Bearing of B from A is 295°.
     Distance 40 m.

7.   Bearing of B from A is 245°.
     Distance 10 m.

8.   Bearing of B from A is 280°.
     Distance 40 m.

1.   Bearing of A from B is 245°.

2.   Bearing of A from B is 070°.

3.   Bearing of A from B is 280°.

4.   Bearing of A from B is 120°.

5.   Bearing of A from B is 295°.

6.   Bearing of A from B is 115°.

7.   Bearing of A from B is 065°.

8.   Bearing of A from B is 100°.

Exercise 16.8: Extension questions

1.   **(a)** (i) 120°; (ii) 10°   **(b)** (i) 90°; (ii) 7.5°   **(c)** (i) 30°; (ii) 2.5°

2.   **(a)** 125°   **(b)** 7.5°   **(c)** 130°

3.   **(a)** $\angle$ EOD = 120°   4.   **(a)** $\angle$ CAF = 45°   5. $\frac{1}{3}$
     (b) $\angle$ DEO = 30°   **(b)** $\angle$ BAF = 105°
     (c) $\angle$ DEC = 90°   **(c)** $\angle$ BAF = 90°
     (d) $\angle$ DEA = 60°   **(d)** $\angle$ BCD = 75°
                                         (e) $\angle$ BFD = 60°
                                         (f) $\angle$ BCD = 180°

Exercise 16.9: Summary exercise

1.   **(a)** Check pupils' drawings for accuracy and neatness. AC = 5.9 cm

     (b) Check pupils' drawings for accuracy and neatness. $\angle$ ZXY = 74°

2.   **(a)** $x = 82°$ (angles of a straight line add up to 180°).

     (b) $x = 53°$ (angles of a triangle add up to 180°).

     (c) $x = 105°$ (vertically opposite angles are equal).

(d) $x = 52°$ (angles at a point add up to 360°).

$y = 80°$ (angles in a triangle add up to 180°).

(e) $x = 97°$ (angles on a straight line add up to 180°).

$y = 26°$ (angles in a triangle add up to 180°).

$z = 37°$ (angles in a triangle add up to 180°).

3. $x = 88°$

4. Check pupils' drawings for accuracy and neatness.

(a) 053° **(b)** 098° **(c)** 143° **(d)** 008°

End of chapter activity: Non-congruent triangles

For most pupils it is sensible to restrict this to non-congruent right-angled triangles.
The table of results is:

Grid	No. of right-angled triangles
1 by 1	0
2 by 2	1
3 by 3	4
4 by 4	9
5 by 5	16

Square numbers again!

1.

2.

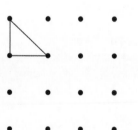 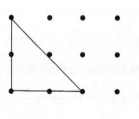 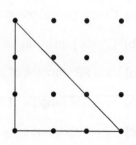

3.

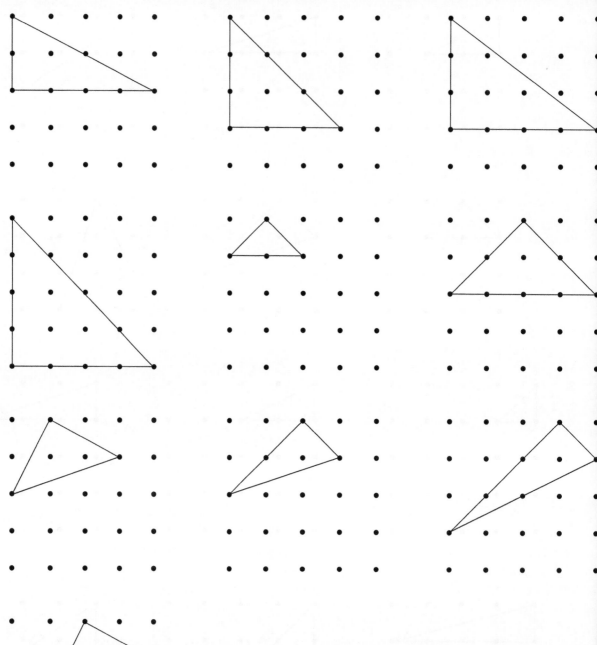

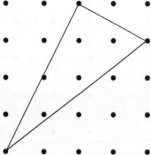

Use any non-congruent triangle as an extension for the more able.

Chapter 17: Percentages

Exercise 17.1

1. **(a)** Check pupils have coloured 10 squares red.
    (b) Check pupils have coloured 3 squares blue.
    (c) Check pupils have coloured 25 squares yellow.
    (d) 62%.
2. **(a)** Check pupils have coloured 15 triangles red.
    (b) Check pupils have coloured 5 triangles blue.
    (c) Check pupils have coloured 30 triangles yellow.
    (d) 50%.
3. **(a)** Check pupils have coloured 50 squares red.
    (b) Check pupils have coloured 35 squares blue.
    (c) Check pupils have coloured 15 squares yellow.
    (d) 0%.
4. **(a)** Check pupils have coloured $\frac{1}{2}$ square red.
    (b) Check pupils have coloured 5 squares blue.
    (c) Check pupils have coloured 10 squares yellow.
    (d) $34\frac{1}{2}$ squares are not coloured; 69%.
5. **(a)** Check pupils have coloured 1 triangle red. 4%.
    (b) Check pupils have cooloured 5 triangles blue.
    (c) Check pupils have coloured 4 triangles yellow.
    (d) 60%.

Exercise 17.2

1. **(a)** $50\% = \frac{50}{100} = \frac{1}{2}$ **(b)** $25\% = \frac{25}{100} = \frac{1}{4}$ **(c)** $10\% = \frac{10}{100} = \frac{1}{10}$

2. **(a)** $20\% = \frac{20}{100} = \frac{1}{5}$ **(b)** $5\% = \frac{5}{100} = \frac{1}{20}$ **(c)** $4\% = \frac{4}{100} = \frac{1}{25}$

3. **(a)** $40\% = \frac{40}{100} = \frac{4}{10} = \frac{2}{5}$ **(b)** $60\% = \frac{60}{100} = \frac{6}{10} = \frac{3}{5}$ **(c)** $80\% = \frac{80}{100} = \frac{8}{10} = \frac{4}{5}$

4. **(a)** $15\% = \frac{15}{100} = \frac{3}{20}$ **(b)** $90\% = \frac{90}{100} = \frac{9}{10}$ **(c)** $65\% = \frac{65}{100} = \frac{13}{20}$

5. **(a)** $35\% = \frac{35}{100} = \frac{7}{20}$ **(b)** $55\% = \frac{55}{100} = \frac{11}{20}$ **(c)** $75\% = \frac{75}{100} = \frac{3}{4}$

6. **(a)** $8\% = \frac{8}{100} = \frac{2}{25}$ **(c)** $24\% = \frac{24}{100} = \frac{6}{25}$ **(e)** $48\% = \frac{48}{100} = \frac{12}{25}$

    (b) $72\% = \frac{72}{100} = \frac{18}{25}$ **(d)** $13\% = \frac{13}{100}$ **(f)** $14\% = \frac{14}{100} = \frac{7}{50}$

Exercise 17.3

1.	65%	5.	15%
2.	70%	6.	10%
3.	85%	7.	20%
4.	70%	8.	25%

Exercise 17.4

1.	£5	4.	20 g
2.	£6.50	5.	0.3 km
3.	20p	6.	0.5 kg

7.	£12	10.	160 g
8.	£5	11.	0.8 km
9.	£1.40	12.	1.6 kg

13.	£24	17.	7.2 kg
14.	£210	18.	3 km
15.	200 g	19.	36 minutes
16.	320 m	20.	20 cm

21.	£27	25.	4.75 kg
22.	£30	26.	4.4 km
23.	140 g	27.	312 g
24.	510 m	28.	1 hour and 21 minutes

Exercise 17.5

1.	£7.50	9.	2.45 kg
2.	£15	10.	3 m
3.	£1	11.	2.5 kg
4.	£10	12.	50 g
5.	0.75 kg	13.	60 m
6.	50 m	14.	0.25 kg
7.	200 g	15.	150 g
8.	12 minutes	16.	0.75 km

Exercise 17.6

1.	0.06	**6.**	0.72	**11.**	0.5	
2.	0.13	**7.**	1	**12.**	0.2	
3.	0.52	**8.**	2	**13.**	0.4	
4.	0.65	**9.**	1.5	**14.**	0.89	
5.	0.04	**10.**	0.75	**15.**	0.03	

Exercise 17.7

1. $\frac{1}{2}$ 0.52   55%

2. $\frac{1}{4}$ 0.26   27%

3. 0.12 $\frac{1}{8}$ 13%

4. 72% $\frac{3}{4}$ 0.77

5. $\frac{1}{5}$ 0.21   22%

6. $\frac{7}{10}$ 78%   0.79 $\frac{4}{5}$

7. $\frac{9}{10}$ 0.909   0.92   95%

8. $\frac{3}{5}$ $\frac{13}{20}$ 65%   0.66

9. $\frac{2}{5}$ 0.414   42% $\frac{9}{20}$

10. $\frac{3}{10}$ 0.308 $\frac{3}{8}$ 38%

Exercise 17.8

1.	25%	**6.**	40%	**11.**	30%	
2.	50%	**7.**	40%	**12.**	25%	
3.	20%	**8.**	80%	**13.**	20%	
4.	75%	**9.**	60%	**14.**	Maths	
5.	20%	**10.**	12.5%			

Exercise 17.9

1. 21p

2. £20

3. (a) £9
   (b) £150
   (c) £28.13

4. 825 g

5. (a) £11.61
   (b) £2.25
   (c) £28.80

6. He leaves a tip of £6. Altogether the meal costs him £46.

7. Dad

8. 18p

Exercise 17.10: Extension questions
Percentages and symmetry

1. Check pupils' own answers. 25 blue squares; 40 yellow squares.
2. Check pupils' own answers. 30 blue; 20 red; 40 yellow.

Exercise 17.11: Summary exercise

1. **(a)** Check pupil has drawn a 10 x 10 square and coloured 12 squares red and 20 squares blue.

   (b) 68%

2. 66%

3. **(a)** $25\% = \dfrac{25}{100} = \dfrac{1}{4}$ **(d)** $24\% = \dfrac{24}{100} = \dfrac{6}{25}$

   (b) $20\% = \dfrac{20}{100} = \dfrac{1}{5}$ **(e)** $35\% = \dfrac{35}{100} = \dfrac{7}{20}$

   (c) $75\% = \dfrac{75}{100} = \dfrac{3}{4}$ **(f)** $72\% = \dfrac{72}{100} = \dfrac{18}{25}$

4. **(a)** £4   **(e)** £5

   (b) 150 g   **(f)** 0.5 kg

   (c) 48 cm   **(g)** 60 m

   (d) £90   **(h)** 900 g

5. 60 children

6. 75%

7. $\dfrac{2}{5}$ 0.404   41%

8. **(a)** £32   **(b)** £19.20   **(c)** £2.40

End of chapter activity: A genius test (for fun only!)

1 = Horn on a unicorn

2 = Peas in a pod

3 = Blind mice (see how they run)

4 = Quarts in a gallon

5 = Lines in a limerick

6 = Wives of Henry the Eighth

7 = Wonders of the ancient world

11 = Players on a football team

12 = Signs of the zodiac

15 = Men on a dead man's chest

18 = Holes on a golf course

21 = Dots on a dice

24 = Hours in a day

26 = Letters of the alphabet

29 = Days in February in a Leap Year

32 = Degrees fahrenheit at which water freezes

40 = Days and nights of the great flood

54 = Cards in a pack with jokers

57 = Heinz varieties

60 = Seconds in a minute

64 = Squares on a chessboard

88 = Piano keys

90 = Degrees in a right angle

1001 = Arabian nights

2468 = Who do we appreciate

Chapter 18: Probability

Exercise 18.1

1. – 5. Check pupils' answers.

6.

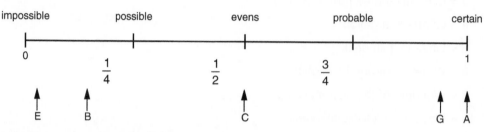

D will depend on the catering staff at the school.

F depends upon how well Chelsea are playing next year and H is variable.

Exercise 18.2

1. $\frac{1}{6}$

2. $\frac{1}{2}$

3. $\frac{1}{2}$

4. $\frac{1}{4}$ (assuming jokers are removed)

5. $\frac{5}{26}$

6. $\frac{2}{11}$

7. $\frac{1}{2}$

8. $\frac{1}{3}$ (if socks are in pairs)

9. $\frac{2}{3}$

10. $\frac{1}{24}$

11. **(a)** $\frac{2}{3}$

   (b) 3 pots

Exercise 18.3

1. **(a)** $\frac{1}{2}$ **(b)** $\frac{2}{5}$ **(c)** $\frac{3}{10}$ **(d)** $\frac{3}{5}$

2. **(a)** $\frac{1}{13}$ **(b)** $\frac{1}{4}$ **(c)** $\frac{1}{52}$ **(d)** $\frac{3}{13}$

3. Line symmetry: A B C D E H I M

   Rotational symmetry: H I N

   (a) $\frac{3}{7}$ **(b)** 0   **(c)** 0   **(d)** $\frac{3}{14}$ **(e)** $\frac{11}{14}$

4. **(a)** $\frac{2}{3}$ **(b)** $\frac{5}{6}$ **(c)** $\frac{2}{3}$

Exercise 18.4

1. (a) $\frac{3}{7}$ (c) $\frac{1}{2}$

   (b) $\frac{4}{7}$ (d) $\frac{1}{2}$

2. (a) $\frac{1}{3}$ (d) $\frac{3}{4}$

   (b) $\frac{1}{6}$ (e) $\frac{3}{11}$

   (c) $\frac{1}{2}$ (f) $\frac{3}{11}$

3. (a) $\frac{1}{3}$ (d) $\frac{11}{23}$

   (b) $\frac{2}{3}$ (e) $\frac{19}{23}$

   (c) $\frac{1}{2}$

Exercise 18.5: Extension questions

1. (a) $\frac{1}{2}$ (b) $\frac{1}{2}$

2.

Team 1	Team 2
A	B
A	C
A	D
A	E
B	C
B	D
B	E
C	D
C	E
D	E

(a) $\frac{2}{5}$ (b) $\frac{2}{5}$

3. (a)

My number	My friend's number	Sum of our numbers
1	2	3
2	4	6
3	6	9
4	8	12
5	10	15
6	12	18
7	14	21
8	16	24
9	18	27
10	20	30

(b) $\frac{1}{2}$ (c) 1

4. (a)

First number	Second number	Sum of our numbers
1	2	3
1	3	4
1	4	5
2	1	3
2	3	5
2	4	6
3	1	4
3	2	5
3	4	7
4	1	5
4	2	6
4	3	7

(b) $\frac{1}{6}$ (c) $\frac{2}{3}$ (d) 5; $\frac{1}{3}$.

5. (a) $\frac{1}{6}$ (b) $\frac{1}{6}$ (c) $\frac{1}{2}$

6. (a) $\frac{1}{3}$ (b) $\frac{1}{6}$ (c) $\frac{1}{2}$

Exercise 18.6: Summary exercise

1. Variable

2. Variable

3. **(a)** $\dfrac{2}{5}$ **(b)** $\dfrac{3}{5}$

4. **(a)** $\dfrac{1}{6}$ **(b)** $\dfrac{1}{2}$ **(c)** $\dfrac{2}{3}$ **(d)** $\dfrac{1}{2}$

5. **(a)** $\dfrac{1}{2}$ **(b)** $\dfrac{2}{13}$ **(c)** $\dfrac{1}{13}$ **(d)** $\dfrac{1}{26}$

6. **(a)** $\dfrac{3}{5}$ **(b)** $\dfrac{3}{10}$ **(c)** $\dfrac{9}{10}$ **(d)** $\dfrac{1}{3}$ **(e)** 0

End of chapter activity: Probability experiments

Practical. Check pupils' answers.

Chapter 19: Shapes in 3 dimensions

Exercise 19.1

1. – 5. Check pupils' drawings.

Exercise 19.2: Drawing more complex solid shapes

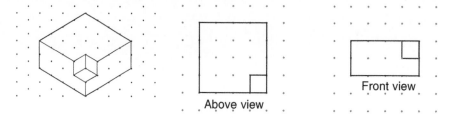

1. Check pupils have made the above shape correctly.

2. Check pupils have made the shape correctly.

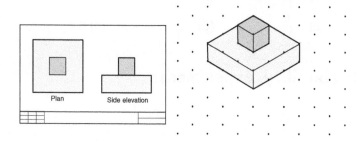

3. Check pupils have made the shape correctly.

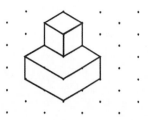

4. Check pupils have made the shape correctly.

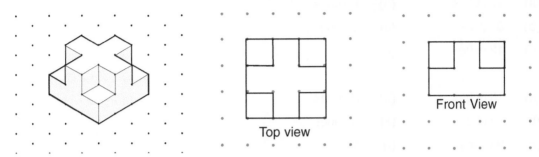

Top view

Front View

5. Check pupils have made the shape correctly.

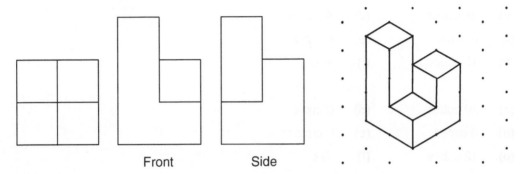

Front   Side

Exercise 19.3

For questions 1 – 5 check pupils have drawn a net as below, and that the measurements are as asked for in the question.

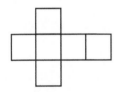

1.   Surface area: 76 cm²

2.   Surface area: 38 cm²

3.   Surface area: 62 cm²

4.   Surface area: 22 cm²

5.   Surface area: 54 cm²

Exercise 19.4: Painting faces

1. **(a)** 27 cubes   **(d)** 6 cubes
    (b) 8 cubes   **(e)** 1 cube
    (c) 12 cubes   **(f)** Yes

2. **(a)** 18 cubes   **(d)** 2 cubes
    (b) 8 cubes   **(e)** 0 cubes
    (c) 8 cubes   **(f)** Yes

3. **(a)** 24 cubes   **(d)** 4 cubes
    (b) 8 cubes   **(e)** 0 cubes
    (c) 12 cubes   **(f)** Yes

4. **(a)** 20 cubes   **(d)** 0 cubes
    (b) 8 cubes   **(e)** 0 cubes
    (c) 12 cubes   **(f)** Yes

Exercise 19.5

1. **(a)** 30 cm³   **(b)** 300 m³   **(c)** 60 cm³
2. **(a)** 64 cm³   **(b)** 64 000 cm³   **(c)** 0.064 cm³
3. **(ii)** 65 cm (the cuboid)

Exercise 19.6

1. **(a)** 7 cm   **(b)** 18 cm   **(c)** 2.4 cm
2. **(a)** 129.6 cm³ or 0.1296 m³   **(b)** 5.376 m³   **(c)** 2.16 m³

Exercise 19.7

1. **(a)** 1000 cm³   **(b)** 10 000 cm³   **(c)** 500 cm³   **(d)** 1200 cm³

2. **(a)** 20 l   **(b)** 360 l   **(c)** 24 000 l

3. **(a)** 10 cm   **(b)** 25 cm   **(c)** 10 cm

4. **(a)** 1000 ml   **(b)** 400 ml   **(c)** 30 cm³

5. **(b)**

Exercise 19.8: Square and cube numbers

1. (a) 1
    (b) 4
    (c) 9
    (d) 16

2. (a) 3
    (b) 5
    (c) 7
    (d) 9

3. (a) 1
    (b) 8
    (c) 27
    (d) 64

4. (a) 7
    (b) 19
    (c) 37
    (d) 61

5. 7   19   37   64

       12   18   24   First difference

         6   6   Second difference

6. Here is the pattern of odd numbers that Fibonnacci produced:

    1

    3   5

    7   9   11

    13   15   17   19

    21   23   25   27   29

    31   33   35   37   39   41

    43   45   47   49   51   53   55

    $1 = 1 = 1 \times 1 \times 1 = 1^3$

    $3 + 5 = 8 = 2 \times 2 \times 2 = 2^3$

    $7 + 9 + 11 = 27 = 3 \times 3 \times 3 = 3^3$

    $64 = 4 \times 4 \times 4 = 4^3$

    $125 = 5 \times 5 \times 5 = 5^3$

    $216 = 6 \times 6 \times 6 = 6^3$

    $343 = 7 \times 7 \times 7 = 7^3$

7. $1 = 1^2$

    $1 + 3 + 5 = 9 = 3^2$ $9 - 1 = 8$

    $1 + 3 + 5 + 7 + 9 + 11 = 36 = 6^2$ $36 - 9 = 27$

    $1 + 3 + 5 + 7 + 9 + 11 + 13 + 15 + 17 + 19 = 100 = 10^2$ $100 - 36 = 64$

    $1 + 3 + 5 + 7 + 9 + 11 + 13 + 15 + 17 + 19 + 21 + 23 + 25 + 27 + 29 =$ $225 = 15^2$

    $1 + 3 + 5 + 7 + 9 + 11 + 13 + 15 + 17 + 19 + 21 + 23 + 25 + 27 + 29 + 31 + 33 + 35 + 37 + 39 + 41 = 441 = 21^2$

8. 1, 3, 6, 10 are triangle numbers.

    Yes, this pattern always works.

    To have a difference of 1000 or 10^3, take the (tenth triangle number)^2 – (ninth triangle number)^2 i.e. $55^2 - 45^2 = 10^3$

9. 1^3 needs 7 dots $(2^3 - 1^3)$

    2^3 needs 19 dots $(3^3 - 2^3)$

    3^3 needs 37 dots $(4^3 - 3^3)$

    4^3 needs 61 dots $(5^3 - 4^3)$

    The sequence is the difference between consecutive cube numbers.

10. Hexagonal numbers are again the difference in cube numbers. This is because they cover the same area on the triangular paper (contain the same number of dots).

Exercise 19.9: Summary exercise

1. Check pupils' drawings.

2. Check pupils' drawings. Surface area = 52 cm².

3. 24 cm³

4. **(a)** On centimetre squared paper.

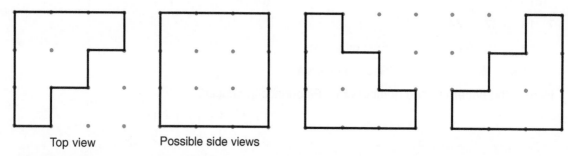

Top view   Possible side views

(b) 23 cm³

5. 2 cm

6. **(a)** 360 cm³

(b) 0.36 l

7. **(a)** 500 cm³

(b) 5 m³

(c) 5000 l

8. 14 cm

End of chapter activity: Make a litre cube

Practical. The strips of paper are available for cutting out on the worksheet.

When you have your litre cubes put them together to show 4 litre, 8 litre and 10 litres.

Pack a cardboard box with your cubes to estimate area. This is a concept that is hard for many children to visualise, and the more practical examples they can see the better.

Chapter 20: Mean, median and mode

Exercise 20.1

1. (a) Range 7; Mean 4

    (b) Range 75; Mean 53

    (c) Range 171; Mean 110

    (d) Range 3; Mean 13

    (e) Range 20.8; Mean 6.2

2. 0.82 m

3. 70 kg

4. (a) 7   (b) 0

5. (a) 6 cm   (b) 15 cm

Exercise 20.2

1. French vocab test marks.

Marks	Tally	Frequency	Total Marks
12	I	1	12
13	III	3	39
14	IIII	4	56
15	III	3	45
16	I	1	16
17	IIII	4	68
18	HHH	5	90
19	II	2	38
20	I	1	20
TOTAL		24	384

The mean mark is 16

Exercise 20.3

1. 216 house points

2. 105 kg

3. **(a)** 13 bottles   **(b)** 24 bottles
4. **(a)** 26 kg   **(b)** 33.2 kg   **(c)** 6.64 kg
5. **(a)** 503.8 kg   **(b)** 552 kg   **(c)** 46 kg
6. **(a)** 1450   **(b)** 73%
7. **(a)** £1.73

    (b) New total £43.40

        Mean before Smith £1.80

        Mean after Smith £1.81

Exercise 20.4

1. **(a)** Median 3   **(d)** Median 13

    (b) Median 36   **(e)** Median 1.2

    (c) Median 92.5

2. **(a)** Median 4;   Mode 1 and 2

    (b) Median 15;   Mode 15

    (c) Median = 8;   Mode 8

3. **(a)** Range 6.1;   Mean 4.1;   Median 3.2;   Mode 3.2

    (b) Range 4.9;   Mean 15.9;   Median 16.3;   Mode 17

    (c) Range 5.89;   Mean 7.43;   Median 8.38;   Mode 9.18

    (d) Range 8.72;   Mean 5.152;   Median 8;   Mode none

    (e) Range 20;   Mean 9.94;   Median 7.06;   Mode none

4. **(a)** His total number of runs was 100, as his range was 100, he must have scored 100 and had 19 innings when he scored 0.

    (b) If her range was 0, she scored the same in every match, namely 5.

    (c) Fred because he can score a century, hopefully he would produce more runs.

         Answers may vary.

Exercise 20.5

1. **(a)**

Mark	Tally	Frequency
16	IIII	4
17	III	3
18	III	3
19	III	3
20	III	3
21	II	2
22	II	2
23	I	1
24	II	2
25	I	1
TOTAL		24

(b) 9

(c) Mean 19.5; Mode 16; Median 19

(d) All the marks were quite similar, as there is a small range and a similar mean, mode and median. (All the class are quite good at spelling.)

(e) A frequency chart to illustrate the marks for the French Vocabulary test:

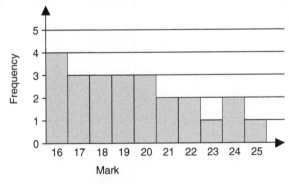

2.

Vehicle	Tally	Frequency
cars	IIII IIII IIII IIII IIII IIII IIII I	36
vans	IIII IIII IIII III	18
bikes	IIII IIII IIII II	17
lorries	IIII III	8
buses	IIII IIII	9
TOTAL		88

(a) Cars.

(b) We are looking at different groups of data. (It's not appropriate.)

3.

Rainfall	Tally	Frequency
0 - 0.9	卌 II	7
1 - 1.9	卌 I	6
2 - 2.9	卌 IIII	9
3 - 3.9	卌 III	8
TOTAL		30

Daily rainfall during April.

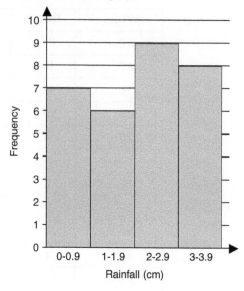

2 - 2.9 is the modal group

4.

Rainfall	Tally	Frequency
0 - 0.9	卌 卌 II	12
1 - 1.9	卌 III	8
2 - 2.9	卌 II	7
3 - 3.9	III	3
TOTAL		30

5. April: Range 3.7 cm; Mean 2.0 cm

June: Range 3.2 cm; Mean 1.37 cm

More rain fell in April. The rain was sometimes heavier in April and the heavier rain occurred more often in April than June. Rain fell on fewer days in June.

Exercise 20.6: Extension question - average age

1. **(a)** 33 years

   (b) 83 years 9 months

   (c) 50 years 4 months

2. **(a)** 11 years   **(b)** 16 years 9 months   **(c)** 12 years 7 months

3. **(a)** 235 years   **(b)** 245 years 5 months   **(c)** 11 years 8 months

4. **(a)** 61 years 8 months (740 months)

   (b) 9 years 4 months (852 months in total)

Exercise 20.7: Summary exercise

1. Mean 1.42; Range 0.15m (15 cm)

2. **(a)** Mean 5.3; Median 5; Mode 4

   (b) Mean 1.9; Median 1.9; Mode 2.1

   (c) Mean 13.4; Median 13.5; Mode 14.1

3. **(a)** 10 years 11 months

   (b) 11 years 11 months

4 (a)

Marks	Tally	Frequency	Total Marks
11	I	1	11
12	I	1	12
13	II	2	26
14	III	3	42
15	IIII	4	60
16	III	3	48
17	II	2	34
18	I	1	18
19	I	1	19
TOTAL		18	270

(b) Mean = 15; Mode = 15; Median = 15

(c) Marks for a mental arithmetic test.

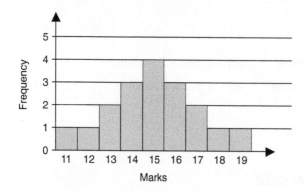

End of Chapter activity: It's time to go!

Practical

Have some maps, atlases and travel brochures ready before you start this bit of cross curricular research. Find some exchange rates (look in the back section of a newspaper).

   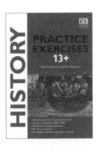 

ISEB
Independent Schools
Examinations Board

This book contains a complete set of answers to So you really want to learn Maths Book 1, a book for Key Stage 3 and Common Entrance.

"This is a book written by a teacher who understands children. There are many attractive features and I expect that children will be inspired by this material. I imagine that this text will enjoy widespread acclaim and become a 'standard' work."

David E. Hanson, Leader of the ISEB 11+ Mathematics setting team, Member of the ISEB 13+ Mathematics setting team, Member of the ISEB Editorial Board

"What a wonderful book: easy to read but so informative, with a clean layout, appropriate diagrams, good cross-curricular presentation, clear instructions and excellent extension exercises for the more able children.

Moira Laffey, The Old Malthouse School

About Galore Park
Galore Park is the leading publisher of high quality educational resources for customers who are aiming for the best academic standards. We produce challenging books and online resources for many of the UK's top schools. Our rigorously produced materials encourage pupils to achieve to the very best of their ability. To take a look at our wide range of resources for teachers, tutors and parents, please visit www.galorepark.co.uk

About ISEB
The Independent Schools Examinations Board (ISEB) offers examinations for pupils transferring from junior to independent senior schools at the ages of 11+ and 13+. The syllabuses are devised and regularly monitored by ISEB, which is composed of representatives from the Headmasters' and Headmistresses' Conference, the Girls' Schools Association and the Independent Association of Preparatory Schools.

ISBN I 90298419-6

9 781902 984193

GALORE PARK

www.galorepark.co.uk